THE EAST-WEST STRATEGIC BALANCE

To Gem

THE EAST-WEST STRATEGIC BALANCE

T.B. MILLAR

London
GEORGE ALLEN & UNWIN
Boston   Sydney

First published in 1981

GEORGE ALLEN & UNWIN LTD
40 Museum Street, London WC1A 1LU

© T.B. Millar 1981

British Library Cataloguing in Publication Data

Millar, T.B.
 The East-West strategic balance.
 1. Balance of power — History
 I. Title
 327.1'12'09 D32
 ISBN 0–04–355015–0
 ISBN 0–04–355017–7 Pbk

Set in 10 on 11 pt Times by
Syarikat Seng Teik Sdn Bhd
Kuala Lumpur

Printed in Hong Kong

CONTENTS

TABLES

ABBREVIATIONS

ABM	anti-ballistic missile
ALCM	air-launched cruise missile
ASW	anti-submarine warfare
AWACS	airborne warning and control system
CIA	Central Intelligence Agency (US)
CMEA or Comecon	Council for Mutual Economic Assistance (Soviet bloc)
CPSU	Communist Party of the Soviet Union
CTB(T)	comprehensive test ban (treaty)
EC or EEC	European Economic Community
FRG	Federal Republic of Germany (West Germany)
FY	fiscal year (US FY 81 began 1 October 1980)
GDR	German Democratic Republic (East Germany)
GLCM	ground-launched cruise missile
IAEA	International Atomic Energy Agency
ICBM	intercontinental ballistic missile
IEA	International Energy Agency
IRBM	intermediate range ballistic missile
LDC	less-developed country
MBFR	mutual balanced force reductions
MIRV	multiple independently-targetable re-entry vehicle
MRBM	medium-range ballistic missile
MRV	multiple re-entry vehicle
NAM	non-aligned movement
NATO	North Atlantic Treaty Organisation
OAS	Organisation of American States

OECD	Organisation for Economic Co-operation and Development
OPEC	Organisation of Petroleum-Exporting Countries
SALT	strategic arms limitation talks
SLBM	submarine-launched ballistic missile
SLCM	submarine-launched cruise missile
SRAM	short-range attack missile
SSBN	ballistic missile submarine (nuclear)
TNF	tactical nuclear forces

PREFACE

This book is an attempt to set down in one place an overview of the strategic balance between the two superpowers, the USA and the USSR, and their allies and associates. As such it is only part of the world scene and a very selective perspective on international events — their causes and courses. Nevertheless the situations and events discussed are of immense importance to everyone on this planet, so great are the explosive forces stored up on both sides, so fragile are some of the political systems that purport or hope to control them.

The International Institute for Strategic Studies, London, annually performs a roughly comparable service through its retrospective *Strategic Survey*. This book is narrower in that it focuses only on key parts of the world strategic picture; it also takes a somewhat longer time scale, and perhaps offers a more personal view.

The nature of the subject — a complex duality — created difficulties for organising the material: whether to examine each power grouping in detail, one after the other; or whether to take a camera slowly around the world, country by country; or to take themes — comparative military capacities, the role of group institutions, the threat of ideologies, ideas, vested interests, technologies. The division and sequence decided upon is a compromise based subjectively on a sense of comparative danger, urgency, and importance. This immediately invites alternative subjectivities and priorities. I make no claim to infallible prescience. One or more of the 'areas of competition' may turn out to be more destructive to world peace than any of the 'areas of danger' So be it. None of the latter may turn out to be very dangerous at all. What a relief that would be.

The book does not attempt to set out in detail the military capacities of the relevant countries. An interested reader should refer, as I have done, to publications of the International Institute for Strategic Studies, the Stockholm International Peace Research Institute, the Research Institute for Peace and Security in Tokyo, and similar bodies, as well as those of the various Western ministries or departments of defence.

Much of the research for this volume was carried out in 1979–80 while I was Academic-in-Residence at the Australian Department of Foreign Affairs, Canberra. I am most grateful for the interest and support of the officers of the Department, especially Sir Nicholas Parkinson and Mr Peter Henderson, who were (in succession) Secretary while I was there. While I have had the benefit of Departmental advice, and of consultation with other branches of government including the Office of National Assessments, the opinions in this work are my own and do not in any way purport to represent the Australian government or any of its departments.

I owe much to colleagues at the Australian National University and to other friends who made valuable comments on drafts of this book. I would like especially to acknowledge the help or support of Alyson Bailes, Coral Bell, Murray Bourchier, Ashton Calvert, Bill Fox, Cheryl Hood, Geoffrey Jukes, Tim McLennan, Bruce Miller, Robert Miller, Jim Morley, Robert O'Neill, Harry Rigby, Robin Ward and John Weltman. I have a permanent indebtedness to the International Institute for Strategic Studies — first to the late Alastair Buchan, and to Kenneth Hunt, Christoph Bertram, Arthur Majendie, and ever-helpful members of the staff. Drafts were typed with cheerful efficiency by Pauline Fingleton, Kathy Earley, Mary Aloisi and Gay Baker. The maps were drawn by Mr M.U. Pancino, Department of Human Geography, Australian National University.

As a young army officer, it was my experience to be one of the first Australians to see Hiroshima after World War II. It was appalling and chastening, and yet, in the context of a frightful conflict just ended, unusual mainly for being so much devastation created by one explosion and gathered in one place. Today we see the Hiroshima bomb as such a little, simple bomb compared with the great missile arsenals of the nuclear powers. If only we still had just a handful of 20-kiloton weapons available, instead of the capacity to destroy the greater part of civilisation and mankind!

It is tempting to see the world as sliding inevitably to a nuclear Armageddon, and yet to use the word 'inevitable' is an abdication of reason. There is no blind force compelling a descent to annihilation. Man is a political being. He thinks, therefore he survives. It is not simply a declaration of faith, cleaving, like Tennyson's sage, to the sunnier side of doubt, but a perception of fact that, for all our fears and alarms, our misunderstandings and mistakes, the balance of intelligence and effort is not on the side of war but on the side of avoiding war, not on the side of destruction but on the side of survival.

T.B.M.
Canberra, December 1980.

INTRODUCTION

If, in 1945, someone had predicted the present state of the global strategic balance, probably no-one would have believed him. Who could have credited that, a third of a century after the end of World War II, Europe would still be an armed camp, with battle lines drawn up; that the United States could still have 200 000 soldiers in Europe, plus air units and missiles, and Britain 50 000; that Germany would still be divided; that the Soviet Union would have 19 divisions in East Germany, 5 in Czechoslovakia, 4 in Hungary, 2 in Poland, 5 or more in Afghanistan, 3 in Mongolia; that both the Americans and the Soviets* would have a capacity to eliminate with nuclear weapons every major city and town, every industrial area, every military base and communications centre, at a few minutes' notice, in the opposite group of countries, with the potential annihilation of hundreds of millions of innocent people? Who would have credited that, with such an enormous overkill capacity, both sides would go on building ever more effective, more devastating weapons of destruction? Or that Britain, France and the Chinese People's Republic would have strategic nuclear weapons directed at the Soviet Union? Or that India, with a demonstrated nuclear explosive capacity, as well as Pakistan, Israel and South Africa, would appear to be leading the proliferation of nuclear weapons states irrespective of the military dangers, the political, economic and social costs, and the evidence that such proliferation appears irreversible? A visitor from outer space could only conclude from these and other manifestations that a large part of mankind had taken leave of its senses.

---

* All writing on this subject in English runs into the problem of how to refer to the people of the USSR collectively and as a nation. To speak of them as 'the Russians' is to include in that term many millions of Soviet citizens who are not ethnically Russian at all. The term 'Soviets' is even more incongruous etymologically, but the usage is widespread and increasing and I have accordingly though reluctantly adopted it.

The atomic explosions at Hiroshima and Nagasaki that ended World War II are the only ones ever used as acts of war. The hope or expectation that the discovery of explosive atomic power would eliminate war has proved as illusory as the similar earlier belief about the discovery of dynamite. The development of nuclear armouries and of only partially effective institutional arrangements to control them, has deterred hostilities between the two superpowers and their allies but has not appeared to deter other conventional (i.e. non-nuclear) conflicts or acts of political hostility. Several scores of wars have occurred, and small states without nuclear weapons have not hesitated to take advantage of the political constraints of the international system which may prevent or deter nuclear weapons states from using their massive destructive capabilities. Thus Yugoslavia for more than thirty years has held out against incorporation into the Soviet empire; Indonesia, Egypt, the Sudan and Somalia ejected the extensive Soviet military and civilian presence that they had previously invited. Various countries, most notably Iran, have thumbed their noses at the United States. The Vietnam war is of a different order in that while the United States both omitted to use nuclear weapons and failed to win the conflict, the extraordinary country ranged against it was aided by two nuclear weapons states, the Soviet Union and the Chinese People's Republic. Yet since Nagasaki, except in the final stalemate stage of the Korean War and possibly in the Taiwan Straits crisis of 1958, the United States has not used even the threat of its nuclear capacity against a state unarmed with nuclear weapons.

Nevertheless, that nuclear weapons have not been used in 36 years proves nothing beyond that fact and the fact that no-one has any experience of a two-sided nuclear war. The armouries exist, and are a constant and constantly changing factor in the global strategic pattern of power. A key question of these times is whether a temporary and partial Soviet superiority over the United States may prompt the Soviet Union to take advantage of that superiority, or of the lack of confidence which a belief in that superiority may engender in Washington.

This work is concerned with the strategy of power as at the present moment and for the next few years — not for every country, but for the United States and the Soviet Union, and the groups of countries associated with them by military agreements. There are of course other configurations and confrontations, but the American-Soviet strategic relationship is the central one for 'international peace and security', the pre-eminent landmark of the international scene. The words 'West' and 'East' are used to refer to these two groups of states. Significant states outside the two groups, such as China, and the main non-aligned countries, will be considered as they relate to the East-West balance.

The word 'strategic' may need some definition. National strategy is the deployment of the nation's physical and psychological resources towards achieving assumed national objectives. There is not space in this work to detail and evaluate all such resources in the two groups of states, or to consider domestic imperatives or objectives. This study attempts to assess political, military and economic policies and capacities able to or designed to change significantly the international political status quo or to prevent such change. In line with current usage, when referring to nuclear weapons, the word 'strategic' in general relates to weapons capable of being used against the Soviet* or American homelands. The term 'superpower' is used only with respect to the Soviet Union and the United States.

It is essential in a study of this kind to keep in mind that one is dealing less with objective facts than with perceptions about them. National interests, hopes and fears are all perceptions. There *are* objective facts, of course — of geography, populations, weapons systems, gross national product, treaties, and so on. These are important, but how they are perceived, by whoever perceives them, is even more important. Some years ago I asked a Japanese official whether he feared the development in China of nuclear weapons. He said that he did not; that the Chinese would never use such weapons against Japan. If they ever threatened to do so, Japan would know it was bluff, and one did not fear what was known to be bluff. The images which the two superpower governments have of themselves and of each other determine their actions. Such images may well be significantly erroneous, may involve a good deal of self-deceptions and self-flattery, even self-serving, by political leaders who both react to and attempt to manipulate the beliefs and moods of their electorates. If these seem elementary points they are still true. The Cold War and its continuing and potentially catastrophic nuclear confrontation are the result of perceptions and fears entertained in the United States and the Soviet Union, of group images and conventional wisdoms. The development of NATO and of the American nuclear armoury has been based on the belief that Western Europe needed to be defended against Soviet depredations yet it is conceivable that the Soviet Union has never had, and would never have, any intention

---

* It does not include nuclear missiles based in continental Western Europe capable of reaching Soviet territory.

to live other than peaceably with Western Europe.[1] Fortunately, or unfortunately, no Western governments have felt able to make that assumption or take (as they see it) that risk. There are, after all, good grounds for different assumptions, even though misinformation, secrecy and suspicion have given added impulse to the arms race.

The changing states system

The world has become a much more complex place since 1945. The break-up of the European empires has added about a hundred new states to the international system and several thousand international organisations or institutions of a governmental, semi-governmental or non-governmental nature. International or multi-national commercial organisations have proliferated in number and operation. While none partakes significantly of the nature of a supranational government, many have reduced national sovereignty in important ways, and are actors in their own right on the international stage. In the inter-governmental institutions, group pressures are brought to bear, and majority wisdom becomes a factor to consider even if you don't believe it. Everyone wants to appear to be on the side of the current angels and their rhetoric.

This does not mean, as some would claim, that the states system has broken down. Since its rise several centuries ago, the states system has always been transfused by ideas, by political ideologies, religious affinities or hostilities, as well as by economic forces and arrangements. The 'resurgence' of Islam and the power of multi-national corporations are modern variations on old themes. The sun never sets on the notion of empire, but alongside it the state is alive and flourishing and taking a continuing flow of decisions. Except in a very few cases, decisions taken by international institutions are taken by the individual governments composing them. The state is circumscribed in various ways, its rights are teased out or diffused, but it is still the state — or a government acting in its name, on its behalf, and with its 'authority' — that acts, records its vote, raises the funds, provides the arms, opts for peace or war.

It is not, of course, sacrosanct, it is not a single type of fixed mechanism, but is a family of diverse organisms undergoing continuing change from the pressures of events and ideas. One of the trends of these times has been the growth of regional groupings among states, a process that divides from others even as it unites within itself. We see regional agglomeration at work internationally in the steady increase of the European Community, in other regional associations such as the communist Council for Mutual Economic Assistance (CMEA, or Comecon), the Organisation of African Unity (OAU), the Organisation of Petroleum Exporting Countries (OPEC), the Association of Southeast Asian Nations (ASEAN), in Vietnam's occupation of virtually the whole of Indo-China, and in expressed desires for re-unification in Korea and Germany. On the other hand we see in some areas a reverse movement towards 'localism' within states which is evident in the various sub-national 'nationalisms' such as Quebec, the Basques of Spain, the Scottish and Welsh nationalist movements, the Polisario movement in north-west Africa, the break-up of Pakistan, the Kurdish movements of West Central Asia, the Muslim independence forces in the Philippines, divisions in Cyprus, and many more. All of these movements have had a disintegrative effect on the state concerned, but they have also usually compelled it to rally its forces, to adjust in order to contain. Some have a disintegrative effect through cross-national affiliations like the Baluchis and the Kurds. Other disintegrative activities include the rise of sub-national terrorism, and the political manifestations of religious extremism as in Northern Ireland and some Muslim countries. But none of these has destroyed the basic authority and competence of the state, which provides a sense of identity to most citizens however amorphous or pluralistic the society.

The Third World

Most of the new states since World War II belong to what we have come to call the Third World — ex-colonial countries with low average standards of living and, because of the pressure of population on resources, few prospects of lifting them significantly. Understandably preoccupied with the problems of establishing their sovereignty, dignity, and economic viability, these 'less developed' or 'developing' countries have with some success acted upon the guilty and/or humanitarian feelings of wealthier (especially Western) powers, and have sought recompense for past deprivations and humiliation and a more equitable distribution of present resources. Multilateral diplomacy — 'ganging up' at the United Nations or at other international assemblies — has been the main means to this end. Except in the near-monopoly situation of Middle East oil, for several reasons the success of this strategy has been restricted and patchy. There is a limit to which even governments in wealthy countries can divert resources away from domestic to foreign consumers. Too often Third World leaders equated rhetoric with reason, abuse with passion and demands with rights. Too often their cases were prepared with inadequate professionalism. Frequently, they were divided among themselves. And, fairly or unfairly, East-West political considerations entered the calculations of donor states. Not for the first time in modern history, but never before for so long, a single set of great power relationships, a single confrontation, fluctuating in its temperature but never ceasing to be a confrontation, has dominated international society.

The policies of the superpowers towards the new states during this decolonising period have not been entirely coherent at any time or consistent over time, and cannot be compressed into a few sentences. But one can see patterns that relate to the present East-West strategic balance. The United States, in a spirit of generosity unparalleled in human history and unlikely to be repeated, gave massive aid to the new less developed countries (LDCs) over many years.[2] With this aid went two assumptions: 1 that the United States, through its democratic, capitalist system, had the answers to human problems and if it didn't have them immediately it would use its pre-eminent technology and unflagging energy to obtain them; and 2 that aid so generously given could reasonably be expected to generate gratitude, political sympathy, and national emulation.

The first assumption had some truth in it, but not enough: the problems were too big, too different from the American experience, too little under American control; the human factors, among both donors and recipients, were too obstinate. The United States eventually lost much of its confidence and enthusiasm. The second assumption was, in retrospect, naïve, because it is not only more blessed but often more easy to give than to receive, and gifts made in the hope of reward are not gifts at all but forms of trade which the weaker party may accept but is likely to resent. Outright capitalist systems had been tried and found wanting, in important social and economic respects, even in the wealthy West. How much more wanting did they seem to be in countries where capital has so small a base and so low a rate of accumulation.

Western democratic processes had a certain idealistic appeal to the educated elites in LDCs, but with a very few exceptions the new states had no experience of working so difficult a system. While many of the new states initially demanded or accepted a form of democracy derived from the metropolitan power, almost all of them quickly reverted to an authoritarianism which was all they had ever known. This was much easier to operate and seemed much more able to get done the things they wanted done, especially to sustain the momentum of economic change, but which all too often included the pursuit of personal or tribal ambitions.

There were real grievances against metropolitan or other Western powers which were derived from the colonial experience: resentment against the arrogance of race, against superior economic strength due to a higher technology, against an alien government backed by military force. The imperial power usually, though decreasingly, had made considerable profits from extracting the country's resources, from developing complementary rather than competing economies and from keeping wage rates down. That it also may have stimulated industries, agricultural development, communications, education and health measures and especially political unity, seemed insufficient compensation. The new administrations were almost always inadequately prepared for self-government. To their resentment over genuine grievances they were tempted to add anger, diverting attention from their own failings to the iniquities of others. The European imperial powers and their natural partner, the United States, fitted this bill very well. And for governments battling to keep their populations from starving, the American preoccupation with its quarrel with the Soviet Union, which it seemed determined to import into every corner of the globe and to use as the touchstone for loyalty and fitness to be helped, was remote, artificial and proscriptive.

The Soviet Union, on the other hand, once it had come alive to the opportunities, appeared to many of the new states as much more of a friend and an example. In international assemblies it sponsored and reiterated the LDCs' grievances and demands and, with its East European partners, the USSR voted loyally, if for a long time ineffectively, to have them attended to. Its Marxist approach appeared on the face of things a logical way to overcome the problems of capital accumulation. It was an authoritarian society, thus offering a form of government closer to those of many new nations. The Soviet Union blamed the problems of the Third World on imperialism or neo-imperialism, thus providing the new states with a convenient scapegoat for their own, often inescapable, shortcomings.

It offered less aid than the West, but aid and influence were not directly proportional, as the West demonstrated. With such aid as it gave, the Soviet Union made most of the mistakes and suffered most of the misfortunes that the Western powers made and suffered. Soviet advisers were heavy-handed, patronising and racist. They demanded political sympathy if not loyalty.[3] Moreover the equipment they supplied was often of inferior quality and performance. Their aid programme overall has had only a fraction of the effectiveness of the West's, but it contained a higher proportion of military aid (by which the new governments could maintain their power both internally and against neighbouring states) and incurred for the Soviet Union much less public opprobrium than the West has received.

There are several reasons for this: the Soviet Union was not an imperial power in the eyes of many LDCs; it has been consistently unstinted in its public support of Third World causes (even though in some forums such as UNCTAD it has behaved more like a developed than a developing state); it has played the diplomatic game more rigorously than have Western states (except perhaps France) and it has shown itself much more likely than the US to react firmly, even nastily, to criticism. And, despite the fact that very few states have voluntarily adopted a communist form of government on the Soviet or Chinese models, the Soviet Union and its sympathisers were for some years remarkably successful in selling the notion that communism was in the vanguard of social progress and conducive to economic justice, genuine political independence and 'world peace'. It took a long time for the largely erroneous nature of these claims and for the true nature of the Soviet system to be recognised by many Third World states.

The wealth, power, generosity and psychological vulnerability of the United States as a democracy made it an easy target for the howling mob or the cheap politician, compounding the problems caused by American errors of judgement. Not altogether ready for the international leadership thrust upon it by World War II, the US did the best it could with the means it had — political, military and economic. To stimulate the rebuilding of Western Europe and to preserve its security against a powerful and aggressive Soviet regime was, on its own, a remarkable achievement. But the role of leader of the 'free world', once accepted, was pursued with all the traditional enthusiasm of a successful frontier society. Here were new frontiers to roll back — frontiers of disaster, poverty and ignorance, and an advancing frontier of godless communism bent on subjugating the world. Early American successes eventually only served to emphasise the disenchantment with both roles which climaxed in the humiliation in Vietnam and forced the United States to acknowledge the limits to which, in a democracy, with the best will and motives, power can be extended into other sovereign states. American power and will nevertheless remained the basic strengths of the West and offered the principal physical defence of Western values and ideals.

The lessons learned by Washington have yet to be absorbed by Moscow,[4] with its different will and motives. Conscious as we all are of the defeats of American foreign policy, we tend to forget the more serious setbacks to the Soviet Union. It turned China from an ally into an enemy. It has managed to impose its will only in the already occupied states of Eastern Europe, and Mongolia. Its only military successes have been in the continued subjugation of East

Germany, Hungary and Czechoslovakia, as well as over economically backward Afghanistan. Its most important on-going 'diplomatic' success in advancing international communism and world revolution has been in Cuba, which dropped almost unassisted into the Soviet lap and costs the Soviet exchequer about $8m per day.[5] But its enormous military capacities and continuing mood of expansion are causes for concern, as Chapter 1 discusses.

The permeable confrontation

There is now a vast literature on the Soviet-American confrontation* which began when the Soviet Union showed it had no intention of vacating the political and economic authority over Eastern Europe that World War II had given it, and that it also wanted authority over Greece and parts of Turkey and Iran. Soviet policy was partly intended to prevent further invasions and depredations from the west; it was also simple acquisitiveness given an ideological coloration. The confrontation was one not just of armed forces, but of ideologies, of ideas about man, government, and the international society to which national power, ambitions and armed forces were inextricably attached, eventually dominating the relationship. This confrontation developed a momentum, mythologies and habits of its own, so that it reached out globally to wherever one government felt it could, at reasonable cost, disadvantage the other.

The process that came to be known as detente was intended to mitigate the more extreme forms and dangers of confrontation, for each to accept the dominance of the other in a core area in order better and jointly to 'manage' the international system, and to enable the Soviet Union to take advantage of the greater capacities of Western countries for technological innovation and agricultural production. Many people in the West believed that increased East-West trade would improve the Soviet Union's international behaviour because of the greater stake it would have in maintaining peaceful relations. While trade may have encouraged the Soviet government to allow increased Jewish emigration (under the Jackson-Vanik amendments to the 1973–4 US Trade Reform Bill), as a constraint trade eventually operated more against the West, inhibiting a strong response to the Soviet invasion of Afghanistan.

During the 1970s the processes of detente became frayed at the

---

* A deep-seated aversion to communism had persisted in the United States from the early days of the Russian revolution. It had prompted the US to intervene on the side of anti-Soviet forces in the Russian civil war, and to delay for many years the establishment of diplomatic relations with the USSR.

edges over several more or less concurrent situations: the decline of American self-confidence following Vietnam and Watergate, American reluctance to develop new generation nuclear weapons while negotiating on arms control (SALT II), the break-up of the Portuguese empire in Africa — from all of which the USSR saw no reason not to take advantage. There was also the American post-Watergate preoccupation with human rights, through which, at Helsinki, the Soviets gained the West's legal recognition of the expanded Soviet post-war European boundaries; the continued expansion of Soviet arms at a faster rate than that of the United States; and the dramatic reversal of the US position in Iran. All this, as well as the Soviet invasion of 'non-aligned' Afghanistan, aroused fears for the East-West balance, with added uncertainties stemming from the oil price rises, from a pending change of leadership in Moscow, and a Democratic president in Washington who somewhat dangerously appeared to combine naïveté and shrewdness, resolution and indecision, political pragmatism and an incapacity to work the system of which he was Chief Executive.

At the same time, the United States ceased to be the dominant economic partner in the West. Bonn and Tokyo now treat with Washington/New York as needed equals, not as supplicants. The European Economic Community (EEC) is a major trading bloc, with unified external policies for many purposes. The American economy is still by far the most powerful in the world, but it no longer has the surpluses that made possible a vast aid programme and provided the bank on which political influence could draw.

Yet one of the most curious, and perhaps comforting, developments during the past decade has been the extent to which the economies of the Soviet Union and Eastern Europe have become enmeshed with those of the OECD countries, and dependent on American and Western Europe credits, currently to the extent of about $65 billion. These credits have made possible the purchase of capital and consumer goods by the communist states which are necessary for economic growth and the satisfaction of consumer needs. They have thus helped to contain some of the domestic resentment against the tyranny of the system and its inadequacy to meet the people's needs. Alternatively, although all trade brings benefits to both sides, one could say that Western credits subsidise the Soviet bloc defence budgets and withhold from Western defence spending the funds needed to provide reassurance against the Soviet 'threat'. Yet this is not an argument to cut ice with the farmer in the American Mid-West, the factory worker in Britain, the banker in West Germany, or indeed the relevant ministers of finance and of employment. Nor is it likely to strike a sympathetic chord with LDC governments for whom both Eastern and Western states are parts of an international capitalist economic system in which they (the LDCs) appear to be the inevitable, perpetual losers.

To overcome their economic disadvantage, rather than to eliminate racism or the remnants of colonialism, has now become the chief objective of the LDCs. Hence their promotion of the concept of a 'New International Economic Order' which would recompense the poorer nations for their limited resources, and for the damage they suffer from their weak bargaining positions. They have demanded better terms of trade, assured access to the markets of the developed countries and stable export prices satisfactory to the producers, as well as the supply of capital and technology at preferred rates, much increased economic aid, and joint control of the international economic system. The West has shown some, but not very much, interest in meeting these demands; the Soviet bloc has shown almost none. The main reason, apart from those already mentioned, is that the wealthy and powerful do not easily give up their wealth and power. Everyone has become conscious of the limited nature of physical resources, especially of petroleum-based fuels. In the last 35 years of the twentieth century, the world will double its population to around 7 billion. Expanding technologies ever more thirsty for energy are depleting the world's oil stocks at a rapid rate. As the late nineteenth century saw European powers and the US scramble for resources through the acquisition of colonies, so the late twentieth century is seeing a scramble by other means for the control of resources on land and in the still largely unowned, unexploited seas and seabeds.

Although the world is a far more complex place, with a much more diverse power structure and more constraints on the naked use of national power, nationalism remains the dominant international political force; the satisfaction of national wants is the dominant end of power. In this coming decade, in an increasingly interdependent world where the transmission of information is almost instantaneous, where the destruction of hundreds of millions of people is only half an hour away from a decision to inflict it, where military technology is increasingly diffused, where the unexpected and dramatic seem more probable than the expected and evolutionary, a key international question will be the extent to which the two superpowers compete or co-operate in the acquisition and sharing of the globe's physical wealth.

Spheres of influence

The notion of 'spheres of influence'[6] derives mostly from the nineteenth century, but the process began long before that. In the period since World War II we have come to think of the world as divided basically into two spheres of influence, the Soviet and the American, plus grey areas where the influence of the superpowers overlaps or conflicts, and other parts were neither has any significant 'edge' over other powers. Some people feel that a major power like China or India is also 'entitled' to such a sphere. In recent years the Chinese have coined the word 'hegemonism' as a term of abuse for what they see as Soviet policies of obtaining a sphere of influence in the Asian region. In its simplest form, the Soviet sphere of influence is usually thought of as comprising the member states of the Warsaw Pact plus Cuba, Mongolia, and, for the time being, at least, Afghanistan, Angola, Ethiopia and South Yemen. It is a moot point whether Vietnam has sufficient self-reliance as to be outside the Soviet sphere of influence, and perhaps within a less subservient 'sphere of interest' (see Chapter 6). Most of Latin America has been considered, under the Monroe Doctrine, to be within the United States' sphere of influence. When necessary, to justify this dominance, both powers refer to agreements which in fact simply rationalised an already existing state of affairs: the Warsaw Pact, and the Charter of the Organisation of American States (OAS). There is a far greater measure of independence in the latter than in the former. Western Europe (and some other areas) could perhaps be said to lie within an American sphere of interest, but not in its sphere of influence, such is the degree of sovereignty of the states concerned. It is virtually inconceivable that if a West European state withdrew from NATO, American tanks would force it to recant; if an East European state withdrew from the Warsaw Pact, it is virtually inconceivable that Soviet tanks would *not* move in.

Despite the rhetoric of successive American presidents and secretaries of state, since 1945 the United States has accepted Soviet predominance within what quickly came to be called the Soviet bloc (of states), and the Soviet government accepted American pre-eminence among the Western powers. One can argue whether this largely tacit mutual recognition of relevant spheres is a force for international order or disorder, but it has been a fact of life unaffected by the growing economic interdependence of the two groups of states. Although the populations of some Soviet bloc states have been restive and have forced organisational changes or even changes in the leadership, the Soviet suppression of uprisings in Eastern Europe demonstrated the penalties for deviance and the apparent hopelessness, in the foreseeable future, of a genuine independence. There is virtually no likelihood that the United States or the other NATO powers will go to war in support of the independence of any communist bloc state.* This is due partly to fear of the consequences, and partly to a curious sense in the West that the Soviet Union has some sort of right to act in and for Eastern Europe. This is at least implicitly an acknowledgement of empire. There is today no comparable acknowledgement, any-where, of a United States or other Western empire. Quite the reverse: the American presence in Europe is imported, alien, temporary. Strangely enough, the nearest current parallel to the notion of a Soviet empire is that of Vietnamese predominance over the whole of Indo-China.

So powerful are the superpowers, so ubiquitous their confronta-tion, so bound is their power to contrasting political and economic ideologies and systems, so intense their 'magnetic fields', so extensive have been their spheres of interest and their capacity and readiness to intervene overtly or covertly in national situations, that both have aroused passionate emotions, for and against, around the globe. In the non-communist world there are those who tend to see 'a Red under every bed', and there are others who disparage them, usually including people who want us to believe there are no Reds under any beds, or, if there are, that they either don't matter or are in the vanguard of progress. Is there a pattern to Soviet international strategy? Many Western analysts believe that there is not. They would agree that the Russians will take available opportunities to exert and retain influence, but that this is a very different thing from a will to empire and a blueprint for its achievement. The 'Soviet bear' never has things all its own way. It makes mistakes, it is clumsy, arrogant, muddles along; it is resisted and from time to time, as in Indonesia, Egypt, the Sudan, Somalia, it is thrown out after great expenditures of its cash and effort. It is therefore not to be feared (they say), not to be met on its own terms and with its own weapons, for its structure of influence is a house of cards which local winds will eventually sweep away. After all, the era of gunboat diplomacy has ended.

On the question as to whether the Soviet government has a continuing programme for acquiring influence or power, the only thing we know is that we don't know. It is not always easy to distinguish the taking of an opportunity from the making of one. But whether there is a design or not, there is a global policy* and,

---

* Some support of Yugoslavia is possible, were it to be invaded or threatened with invasion.

* The point has been well put by V. Aspaturian: '... the Soviet Union has developed a global policy, representing an intersection of Soviet global capabilities and re-sidual universalist ideological goals.' ('Soviet Global Power and the Correlation of Forces', in, *Problems of Communism*, Vol. XXIX, No. 3, May–June 1980, p. 16.)

in Soviet terms there has been undoubted progress and achievement. Certainly the Soviets have made mistakes; they have been resisted and even expelled, but, as in Egypt and Indonesia, they may have wrought immense havoc with local or Western interests in the meantime. The net growth in demonstrated influence around the globe has been extraordinary, and if it had been achieved by the United States it would have excited condemnation far more widespread than the Russians have sustained. In country after country where the Soviet Union has a significant and influential presence, that presence has not yet fallen by its own weight nor has it been blown away by nationalist winds. Eight member countries of the United Nations[7] are effectively under Soviet military occupation or political control. There is no comparable American ascendancy, not even the case, often cited by the USSR, of the US hold on Guantanamo naval base in Cuba.[8]

Gunboat diplomacy

As to gunboat diplomacy being dead, this is patently incorrect. It is still true that there is 'no more reason to believe that the days of "gunboat diplomacy" are over than to believe that the threat of force will not be used on land or in the air'[9]. What is the effect of the sight of a warship on the horizon? Who is frightened by such an old-fashioned, blunt instrument of power? In this age of lost empires and ended colonialisms, which are the countries that can get away with the naked use of force against another sovereign state? The effect of a foreign warship will depend on the circumstances of the country against which it is deployed, the objectives of the deployer, what larger elements accompany it or are believed to be behind it, over the horizon, and what other support or pressure may be at hand.

In James Cable's book on the subject[10], under a quite vigorous definition of what constitutes gunboat diplomacy, he lists 82 such incidents between 1945 and 1969 involving as 'assailant' the United States (35 times), Britain (22 times), France (6), South Korea (6), the Soviet Union (3), Nationalist China (2) and once each for Egypt, Canada, Argentina, Japan, Peru, Colombia, the Netherlands, Indonesia, Cuba, Turkey, North Vietnam, North Korea, Israel, Iran and Spain.

A more recent Brookings Institution study[11] investigated 215 incidents since World War II, ranging from a naval vessel visiting a friendly port to the forceable establishment of a military presence when the United States used armed force for political objectives, either to reassure allies or warn opponents. While the Soviet military presence in various countries is not gunboat diplomacy, it is the patent use of military force for political ends, given emphasis by the crushing of revolt in East Germany in 1953, Hungary in 1956, Czechoslovakia in 1968 and Afghanistan (still in progress) in 1979–81. Soviet naval vessels were used as a support for Soviet or Soviet-Cuban political or military operations in Somalia, the Sudan, Egypt, Angola, the Yemen, and Vietnam. Soviet maritime capabilities will be considered later, but their global deployment in recent years is in part *flottenpolitik*, making the Soviet naval presence visible in many places so that it becomes a factor in local political calculations and indicating a potential for gunboat diplomacy.

The Brookings study shows that American use of armed force has usually contributed to the achievement of US objectives in the short term. In most cases it has not greatly changed the major long-run economic or political trends in the country where it has been applied. One could say much the same about several of the across-water interventions of the Soviet Union, but certainly not about all of them, for many are still continuing. And in the Socialist bloc, with a continuing Soviet military presence which ranges up to 19 divisions in the case of the German Democratic Republic, presumably the Soviets feel that their presence is necessary to maintain each country's political alignment. So extensively does the use of force or the supply of arms and military advisers feature in Soviet diplomacy that one could be forgiven for believing it to be the principal instrument of Soviet foreign policy.

The Soviet treatment of Somalia, whether a test case or not, is interesting evidence of Soviet policies. A small African dictatorship with strong ethnic-based grievances against its neighbours was offered military aid by the Soviet Union. Soviet influence grew so that before long the small Somali defence forces were armed, trained and advised by the Soviets. An internal security service was trained, advised and permeated by the Soviets and their influence dominated the internal political organisation and foreign policy. A Soviet dry dock was available to service Soviet ships by then deployed in the Indian Ocean. A Soviet missile storage facility and a communications station were erected. Somalia appeared close to becoming a Soviet dependency. Then came the revolution in Ethiopia, and the Soviet government took advantage of the orientation and weaknesses of the new Ethiopian government to offer similar kinds of help there. The offer was accepted, but this so antagonised Somalia (with irredentist claims to the Ethiopian Ogaden region) that it ordered all Soviet representatives out of the country. With scarcely a murmur (so far as we know), they went, quickly giving up an investment that had been costly by any criteria, and dismantling the movable parts of the facilities they had erected.

There could be several explanations for the prompt Soviet withdrawal. One stems from the hypothesis that the Soviet Union sets much store by legal forms and believes that the Somali government was entitled to act as it did, unhelpful though that was. Another is that, in assisting Ethiopia, the Soviet government realised that it would be involved in a conflict between two neighbours; that it could not possibly fight on both sides, and so it backed the strongest — or, in Soviet terms, the most valuable — horse. Somalia also showed that it could make things very uncomfortable for the Soviets. Whatever the explanation, the situation seemed to indicate that the Soviet government has, or had at that time, no will to empire across water, and no will to subjugate an alien people and territory without the kind of international cachet that a wider war provided. Unfortunately, more recent evidence in Afghanistan disproves the second thesis and suggests that the will to empire, to territorial and political expansion, exerts itself wherever the leadership feels the circumstances require or are favourable to it.

To assess the strategic significance of Soviet power, we must relate it to peacetime no less than to war. Most of the world, after all, is far more often at peace than it is at war. Yet much of the Western and Third World analysis of Soviet military activities outside its continental environment, disparages them on the grounds that they would be of little value in the event of major war. Therefore, goes the implication, they are of little value in peace. This is nonsense. It ignores the world of power politics. It ignores the psychological effects of real or imagined military strength or weakness. It ignores the reasonable proposition that major war is the least likely kind of war we will have, whereas minor conflict appears endemic. It too sweepingly discounts, in advance of the evidence, the capacities of remote deployments. American help to Israel in the 1973 war depended on the existence of Portugal's Azores base; in a subsequent war it could depend on bases in Australia, or at Diego Garcia in the Indian Ocean. The Soviet-Cuban intervention in Angola was made possible by the ground prepared in Guinea.

Sino-Soviet split

The East-West confrontation which seemed so firmly set by 1950 was almost global in character. On the one side were the United States and the European empires; on the other the Soviet Union with its new domains in Eastern Europe, and the Chinese People's

Republic with a quarter of the world's population. The break-up of the European empires changed the nature of world society, rearranged the priorities of international discourse and provided opportunities for superpower competition at the widening margins of influence. The Sino-Soviet split of 1959–60, a more abrupt but less understood development, fundamentally changed the East-West strategic balance yet it was more than a decade before this change began to 'bite' on the international system. This was due to the legacy of hostility between the United States and communist China, to China's continuing pursuit of radical communist policies at home with rhetoric to encourage them abroad and to American involvement in the Vietnam war, where China and the Soviet Union had little choice but to be joint if uneasy allies of the Democratic Republic of (North) Vietnam.

The implications and potential durability of the Sino-Soviet 'Cold War with hot flushes' is discussed in Chapter 6. It has transformed the east Asian stategic scene by inducing the Soviet Union to deploy immense forces (more than 40 divisions, plus aircraft, missiles and naval forces) in its eastern region, primarily against China. It has promoted a loose coalition of interests between China, Japan and the United States, and encouraged the post-Mao leadership in China to look to the West for the capital, technology and ideas needed to 'modernise' the country, and perhaps also for the arms to defend it. It has meant that the Soviet Union has fewer forces at its 'frontdoor' in Europe but that it has a continuing worry about its back door in Asia. This must act as a constraint on Soviet adventures. It must also reinforce their sense of being beleaguered in a fortress, physically and psychologically, of needing to be ever more powerful, of requiring their peoples to stick together, of being cautious about any internal concessions that might upset the political stability and thus the physical defence of the motherland.

Invasion of Afghanistan

The Soviet invasion of Afghanistan in late 1979 (see Chapter 5) marked a watershed in the perceptions held by the West — indeed, by the world outside the Soviet bloc — of the East-West strategic balance. It came so soon after the fall of the Shah of Iran, the ending of America's special relationship with that country and the seizure of its diplomats as hostages, and it aroused, revived or confirmed fears of the Soviet Union as an imperialistic, military power. In an unprecedented move, more than 100 members of the United Nations condemned the invasion. The conference of Islamic states, including some who would normally prefer not to antagonise the Soviet Union, also condemned it. The United States, whose retreat from its role as 'world policeman' and from most of what that involved, had long been slowing down, was brought up with a jolt. The landslide election of President Reagan in November 1980 was a demonstration of a new American mood, a reassertion of national dignity and power and determination not to be 'pushed around'.

Afghanistan was a catalyst to a variety of developments. It troubled the Soviet bloc, bringing public reproof from Romania. It complicated action to restrain Poland's free trade union movement and thus gave an indirect impulse to that movement. It stimulated defence spending in NATO. Within the Western alliance and between the US and the USSR, it exposed differences of view on the nature and value of detente. When the US called for sanctions, it provided a practical test of the solidarity of NATO and, incidentally, of the European Community. It accelerated American moves to set up a Rapid Deployment Force for use in the Gulf region, to increase its naval deployments and support facilities in the Indian Ocean. It consolidated anti-Soviet feelings in eastern Asia, strengthening the grounds for co-operation between Japan, China and the United States. It caused scholars and politicians to speak of a 'new Cold War'.

Throughout this work I try to evaluate the importance of Soviet influence in various parts of the world, not *in vacuo* but as one of several influences, and especially in the context of the existence or lack of a countervailing Western influence. It is easy to read too much into a Soviet presence, whether this be a handful of instructors, a visit by a Soviet dignitary or warship, an arms arrangement or a treaty of peace and friendship. Other countries provide arms, aid, visitors, treaties. The Soviet Union is a superpower but its citizens are not a race of supermen: they are a patient and dogged people. Their leadership is highly authoritarian, nationalistic, chauvinistic. They have immense military might and great confidence in their capacity to use it. On the whole they pursue their own national interest by means not so very different from those used by Europeans and Americans in the past. They have their entrances and their exits. They give no sign of wanting to set the world on fire even though they have the instruments to do so, but they have demonstrated a capacity for the use of military force across their borders. They give evidence of being an unsatisfied power, of requiring (in the interest of the rest of us) to be contained.

Until the invasion of Afghanistan, this was all in strong contrast to the United States, the leader and basic strength of the West, whose military power and apparent will to use it, compared with that of the Soviet Union, had noticeably declined. The US would have withdrawn its forces from South Korea if it reasonably could have done so, and probably it would eventually have been prepared to withdraw from Western Europe. It had receded a considerable distance from its desire and ability to contain Soviet ambitions outside the European continent. For 14 long months it was the subject of almost unbearable humiliation by a handful of 'students' in Tehran.

As the world moves through the decade of the 1980s, the dominant new factors in the East-West strategic balance are the expanded power and outreach of the Soviet Union and the reawakened will and resistance of the United States. Outside the Soviet bloc, the first is much less reassuring than the second, but if not carefully managed both are potential sources of danger. Both are occurring at a time when there are far more restraints upon the uses of great power than in the time of the European empires: restraints imposed by the widespread diffusion of political authority and of modern armaments, by the multiplicity of earnest international institutions, and by the pressing, exploding needs of a rapidly expanding world population.

1   THE SOVIET IMPERIAL SYSTEM

It is sometimes said that the British acquired their empire in a fit of absent mindedness. There is an element of truth in this in that much of the territory that ended up as part of the British empire had its first contact with Britain in the form of explorers, missionaries or traders. 'The flag' — political control — sometimes preceded but often followed these activities. Nevertheless, a bus that runs over you when the driver is looking the other way or thinking about something else is still a bus that runs over you. Moreover, despite the reluctance and equivocation that existed in Westminister and Whitehall, for well over two centuries there existed in the British government and establishment a will to empire varying in degree but effective in operation. So far as we know, there was no formal planning organisation as part of the government in London throughout this period which was calculating how to take over as much of the world as was obtainable at acceptable cost. But there was a conventional wisdom about expanding and protecting trade, and there was a state of mind that went much wider than Westminster and Whitehall which saw the acquisition of territory and the control of their populations as being for the greater glory of 'England' and the fulfilment of its destiny. There was a variety of institutions impelled by such a vision. There was a sense that the British people were, if not a 'master' race, at least a superior one with a superior civilisation and a superior capacity and right to engage against and control less civilised peoples in government, commerce, education and religion. Behind and permeating all the operations of the empire were the threat and ability to use force, often through local or imported proxies.

No two empires are the same in their origins, nature, or extent. There are colonies of settlement and colonies of control. There are empires over water managed by naval power, and empires created by expansion over land through the use of armies. The British empire is not a prototype of all empires, although it had many of the characteristics of imperial ventures throughout history. The irreducible core of meaning of the word 'imperialism' is domination by persons of one nation over another nation, and even though that begs the question of what is a nation,[1] it is enough to demonstrate that what we now know as the Union of Soviet Socialist Republics became what it is by a series of imperialistic expansions spread over several centuries. Since 1938, the Soviet government has added to Soviet territory by threat or force of arms part of Finland, the three Baltic republics of Latvia, Lithuania and Estonia, a large part of Poland, the Romanian province of Bessarabia and the northern part of Bukovina, Ruthenia (from Hungary), half of East Prussia* (from Germany), the southern half of Sakhalin (from Japan), the Kuril Islands (Japan), and the People's Republic of Tanna Tuva. Soviet absorption of these areas and suppression or sublimation of their sense of nationalism has been effected by overwhelming military power, by forced migrations of people and their replacement by Russians, as well as by industrialisation, education, propaganda, concessions to local cultural feelings and by the incorporation of regional leaders in the centralised Soviet power structure.[2]

It is difficult to tell to what extent local 'nationalisms' and considerations of racial affinity or hostility affect loyalties to the Soviet state and system today. Within the USSR there are still many visible elements of a continuing imperialist process, although the highly centralised, highly authoritarian political and economic structure is imposed impartially on a diversified congeries of 'republics' and ethnic minorities.

Much of the process of Soviet territorial expansion since 1919 has been designed for the purpose — or at least has had the effect — of bringing within Soviet boundaries the totality, or a larger proportion, of each of several ethnic groups which hitherto had straddled the border (as a result of earlier conquests): Georgians, Armenians, Ukrainians, Uzbeks, Kazakhs, Azeris, Turkmens, Kirgiz. Where this process has not been completed — notably as with Turkey, Afghanistan and Iran (Azerbaijan), as well as with the Chinese People's Republic — the smaller neighbouring states especially may have grounds for apprehension, as Afghanistan has demonstrated, even though in that case the main reasons for action probably did not include ethnic considerations.

---

* It is appreciated that these areas have come under different sovereignties over the centuries, and that in some the majority of the population were of nationalities (especially Ukranian and Byelorussians) now forming constituent republics of the Soviet Union.

The Soviet empire

But when considering the Soviet Union as an imperial power, i.e. as exercising *now* the functions of empire, we think usually of the states of Eastern Europe plus Mongolia. To what extent are they part of a Soviet empire?

Chronologically, Mongolia was the first. Tsarist Russia had had a prominent influence in Mongolia with special privileges which the Soviet government repudiated in 1919. After a struggle for power involving Mongolian revolutionaries, Chinese, Russians and Japanese, a group of Mongolian exiles just inside Soviet territory formed a 'people's government' of Mongolia, appealed for Soviet aid, and the Red Army marched in. It took over the country and in July 1921 set up a subservient communist government which signed a treaty of alliance with Moscow. Two successive groups of local revolutionary leaders were executed by the occupying power. Since that time, governments of the Mongolian People's Republic have ruled in the shadow of Soviet armed forces, have been composed of Mongolian communists acceptable to the Soviet government and have run their domestic and foreign policies on the advice and with the consent of the USSR. There are the trappings but almost none of the substance of an independent sovereignty. Here was, as it still is, a Soviet colony, or at very least a protectorate.

Finland, which had been part of Sweden until 1809 and then a Russian grand duchy until the 1917 revolution, survived Soviet expansion of the early 1920s partly because of British naval power in the Baltic. It survived a Soviet invasion of 1939–40 through its remarkable courage and stubbornness in the face of vastly superior Soviet arms, and it got away with conceding three strategic pieces of territory — north of Petsamo on the Arctic coast, north and south of Salla, and a large area including Vyborg near Leningrad. Since the war Finland has survived by a mixture of independence from and deference to the Soviet Union, avoiding unnecessary provocations or concessions. It is continuously a hostage to Soviet power, which could easily manufacture a pretext for absorbing it but would pay a heavy political cost.

The establishment of communist governments in Poland, Hungary, Czechoslovakia, East Germany, Romania and Bulgaria after World War II was not due to Churchill's famous 'sharing of predominance' agreement with Stalin in Moscow in October 1944,[3] but to the presence of Soviet armies of liberation and occupation. In Yugoslavia (see Chapter 5), the communist 'partisans' had received help from both Britain and the USSR, but they set up their own government without Soviet participation. The Albanian communist party did the same, though with Yugoslav communist assistance. But the other six, except Czechoslovakia, had local communist or communist-dominated governments backed by Soviet divisions and operating within Soviet constraints. Bulgaria, Hungary and Romania had been allies of Germany and were thus treated as defeated enemy powers. The Soviet army was withdrawn from Czechoslovakia in December 1945, leaving indigenous communists in key positions from which, a little over two years later and with Soviet help and encouragement, they were able to take over government by partly constitutional and partly revolutionary means. The Soviet occupied zone of East Germany was treated as a defeated enemy and plundered accordingly, with semi-democratic systems quickly giving way to an imposed communist constitution and government. In Poland, which had suffered terribly at the hand of the original Soviet occupation of part of the country in 1939–41[4] even if more terribly at the hands of the Germans, the Soviet Union retained its forces, claiming that it needed them for direct communications with its army of occupation in Germany. It eliminated the leaders and middle ranks of the Polish national movement and imposed a puppet government on the country.

By late 1949, all six states had governments completely subservient to Moscow, constitutions modelled on the Soviet constitution, and a communist party modelled on the Communist Party of the Soviet Union (CPSU) with personnel and policies effectively determined by the CPSU. Even though it does not seem that Stalin envisaged incorporation of these states within the Soviet Union,[5] they were as surely a part of a Soviet empire, as directly controlled from Moscow, as any British-controlled territories had been part of the British Empire and controlled from London after the initial stages of settlement. Formal treaties of Friendship, Co-operation and Mutual Assistance with all states except East Germany and Albania provided a legal basis for Soviet intervention and influence. Only Yugoslavia (and later, with Chinese help, Albania[6]) held out against Soviet pressures and proved that it was possible to do so.*

Since the 1950s, the political and social systems of the Soviet

---

* In Asia, the Soviet forces occupying North Korea installed a communist government in Pyongyang along the lines of those in Eastern Europe and provided it with the arms and encouragement that led it to launch a war on the South in June 1950 after most American forces had been withdrawn, and Secretary of State Dean Acheson had publicly put Korea outside the US defence perimeter. This episode will be considered further in Chapter 6. The Sino-Soviet relationship will be discussed in the same chapter, but there is no basis for including China, at any time, within the Soviet imperial system.

Union and of the East European 'satellite' states have all changed in different ways, and their relationships with one another have changed. Those changes are the subject of a growing literature, and are beyond the scope of this study. The question here is the extent to which the Soviet Union still appears to exercise forms of imperial power over them and the implications of this for Soviet policies elsewhere and for the East-West strategic balance.

The Warsaw Pact

The formal military basis of Soviet power in Eastern Europe is the Warsaw Pact of 1955 which was set up as a direct result of West Germany's accession to NATO, which in turn flowed from the suppression of the East German uprising of 1953 and the earlier (1948–9) Soviet attempt to take over West Berlin by a land blockade. The Warsaw treaty is a straight military treaty of alliance, with some striking similarities to the North Atlantic Treaty. The difference between the two treaties lies in the different degrees of sovereignty exercised by member governments. The Western alliance (see Chapter 2) is much looser, its partners more independent, more sovereign, more open, more subject to internal democratic pressures, and to a variety of vested interests, than is the Eastern alliance.

NATO is designed to defend Western Europe. The Warsaw Pact is designed to defend the Soviet Union and its 'empire' in Eastern Europe. What keeps NATO together is a common fear of the Soviet Union. What keeps the Warsaw Pact together is a Soviet-imposed system of control, the presence of Soviet divisions in most member states, a common public dogma, some fear (especially in Poland and in the USSR) of Germany, and (among the ruling elites) an awareness of American military power. A web of bilateral treaties between member states reinforces the effects of the Warsaw Pact itself. The Soviet Union has status of forces agreements with all Pact members except Romania and Bulgaria.

The Warsaw Pact gives little evidence of being a treaty between sovereign, independent states. As a treaty organisation it is controlled formally by a political consultative committee comprising the first secretaries of the communist parties, heads of government, and the foreign and defence ministers of the member governments. The joint secretariat, headed by a Soviet official, and the Permanent Commission, are both located in Moscow. The Commander in Chief is a senior Soviet military officer and he commands the Joint High Command and chairs the Military Council. Most of the key positions are held by Soviet officers or officials. The headquarters of the air defence system is in Moscow. The forces of the member states are operationally subordinate to the Soviet High Command in time of war. It is a highly centralised system, with largely common doctrine, organisation, training, weapons systems and communications.[7] Five members of the Pact invaded undefended Czechoslovakia in 1968 and this invasion was rationalised in Moscow by reference to the Warsaw treaty.

The USSR would prefer the Warsaw Pact members to possess no flexibility in their foreign and defence policies; in fact members do exercise limited independence. It is not proposed to detail here the many differences between the domestic, foreign and defence situations of the Warsaw Pact member states but merely to touch on some key aspects. The evidence suggests that Romania has the greatest degree of independence in that it takes a visibly different line on foreign policy issues (e.g. it clearly frowned on the Soviet invasion of Afghanistan); it has no Soviet troops in the country, does not take a full part in Warsaw Pact manoeuvres and does not always accept Soviet instructions to boost defence spending. Whether this independence would be exerted or exertable in a crisis situation cannot be determined in advance. Romania buys its limited independence in foreign policy with an almost unlimited doctrinal rigidity in domestic policy. Some observers see Romanian policy as 'running to the end of the chain, barking', but it is unlikely that Romania would take part in an attack on Yugoslavia and it would probably do everything it could to discourage the passage of Soviet forces across Romania. It has been repeatedly demonstrated that Romanians, a people of Latin culture, have an intense distaste for the Soviet Union, as well as an irredentist grievance over Moldavia. Bulgaria, also without a Soviet military presence, is considered the most docile of the satellites, a Soviet republic or province in all but name. Bulgaria would probably see a Soviet attack on Yugoslavia as an opportunity to help dismember its neighbour and incorporate the long-desired, ethnically-related province of Macedonia. It is scarcely conceivable that Bulgarian divisions would not be at the service of the Soviet Union in any European situation. And yet there is also evidence that some Bulgarians, as distinct from their communist party leadership, deeply resent the Russians and their own government's subservience to Moscow.

Czechoslovakia was cowed by Soviet suppression of its 'Prague spring' of 1968. Before World War II, Czechoslovakia had one of the highest standards of living in Europe. Now it is much lower. Soviet watchfulness makes it unlikely that Czechoslovakia can hope to be other than a 'loyal ally' of the Soviet Union and politically subordinate. Strategically it is immensely vulnerable, with East Germany, Poland, the Soviet Union and Hungary enclosing it on three sides.

Twelve years before Prague, Hungary suffered suppression by Soviet tanks and it learned a lesson. Hungarians are a calculating people. In their domestic policies they have moved a long way from doctrinaire Soviet communism and they appear to estimate that they can exercise considerable flexibility in economic areas provided they respect the public forms and the limits of deviation in foreign policy allowed by Moscow. In private, Hungarians refer to Hungary as the 'jolliest barracks in the communist world'.

Poland is in a special strategic position: it is the historic invasion route to Russia (Napoleon 1812, Hitler 1941) and it is the essential communications zone from the Soviet Union to the 'seam of Europe' (the East-West German border) and to the 19 Soviet divisions in the German Democratic Republic (GDR). So long as these divisions remain, so long as Moscow sees its front line along that seam, no Soviet government can be expected to allow a threat to Poland's full participation in the operations of the Warsaw Pact. This the Poles understand only too well. By political demonstrations they have forced changes in domestic policies and leadership and even (in 1980–81) in the role and authority of their communist party. By sheer weight of public feeling, they have preserved forms of personal liberty, and especially religious liberty (identified with Polish nationalism), to a degree unknown anywhere else in Eastern Europe.[8] In foreign policy they have repeatedly taken initiatives (such as the Rapacki Plan for nuclear disengagement) designed to ease East-West tensions, but in the essentials of policy they do not deviate from the strict line determined in Moscow.

During the late 1970s, almost unmolested, dissidence began to increase in Poland, feeding on economic mismanagement and agricultural disasters that kept food and consumer goods in short supply. In the second half of 1980, under the impact of consumer price rises, Polish workers once again forced a change of political leadership (although the leadership of the armed forces did not change), and by concerted action they demanded and obtained a 'free' trade union movement ('Solidarity') independent of the Polish Communist Party. This ran dangerously counter to Soviet socialist doctrine and practice, and while Polish government rhetoric was along party lines, in fact the government did more to accommodate than to suppress the movement. Soviet divisions then massed on Poland's borders with both the USSR and the GDR ready to invade. At the time this is being written, they have not invaded. The Soviets are faced with two alternative sets of incalculable consequences: if they do not invade Poland they could find that it increasingly liberalises the political process, allowing free speech, assembly, and even elections, offering an example which some neighbouring East European peoples, including East Germans, as well as the peoples of the USSR, might be tempted to try to emulate. If the Soviet Union does invade Poland, it could destroy most of what is left of detente and the help it renders the Soviet and Soviet bloc economies; it might find the Poles far more resistant than the Hungarians or the Czechs were, and perhaps even prepared, like dangerous animals, to defend themselves. Other East European states would be greatly troubled by such a conflict, which the Soviets would win but at considerable and unpredictable military and political cost.

The Democratic Republic of [East] Germany is the forward battle zone of the Warsaw Pact, the vital ground. 'Prussian' efficiency and national pride, plus a sense of competition with the Federal Republic, have helped to produce the highest standard of living within Eastern Europe. Intra-German trade has become economically significant. Western radio and television programmes cannot be excluded. For all these reasons, the GDR has the least flexibility of all, the least capacity (for the foreseeable future) to go beyond those narrow limits of domestic or foreign policy which protect the frontier of the Soviet European system, the physical and psychological Berlin wall, barbed wire, minefields, soldiers and dogs.

The formal organisation and arrangements of the Warsaw Pact indicate almost total Soviet domination of alliance strategy and deployments. It is certainly a much more disciplined organisation than is NATO. The several member states are controlled by their communist parties. All we know of the relationships between the CPSU and the East European parties (and secret police) suggests that for the most part Soviet control exists at that level in most essential matters, sometimes through formal arrangements and sometimes by more tacit agreement. Within the general loyalty of the East European party leaderships, there are undoubtedly different emphases in policy, different attitudes to the extension of Soviet power, different relations with the US, the countries of Western Europe and the Third World. Polish or Hungarian troops are unlikely to serve in Africa or the Middle East on Soviet missions. But further, all East European governments know that none of them is there through the freely-expressed will of its people, so none can be sure how the people will react in situations other than the highly unlikely event of self-defence against a war launched from the West.* If the basic aim of the Warsaw Pact is seen by

---

* According to reports, the armed forces of the Pact states never have the latest Soviet arms and equipment. This would suggest (a) that they are not wholly trusted by their Soviet mentors, and (b) that in a major war they would be used as second-line, not first-line, forces.

Moscow as the security of the Soviet Union and its European system, thinking citizens of Budapest, Warsaw, Prague, etc. must see it at least as having the effect of maintaining the Soviet grip on Eastern Europe, an effect against which, from time to time, the peoples of Eastern Europe must be expected to rise up in anger.

The countries and peoples of this region are not voluntarily bound together in a common purpose. Their unity, like their national authority, is imposed. They have historic differences which surface from time to time. There is strong animosity between Hungary and Romania over Transylvania. The people of Warsaw and the people of Berlin are Poles and Germans first, and communists second. No Polish diplomat can watch, with any feeling of comfort, a military parade in East Berlin with German soldiers goose-stepping down the Unter den Linden to the tunes of the Kaiser's army. Such comfort as the Pole may feel will derive from the protection of the Warsaw Pact and the division of Germany. Even that cold comfort is denied him when he sees East Germany as part of the mechanism for ensuring a minimum conformity to bloc cohesion and socialist principles.

Seton-Watson has likened the founders of the Russian empire to the founders of the British.[9] But whereas the successors, the ruling classes, in Britain were the new, private bourgeoisie created by the industrial revolution, men of high principle and higher self-confidence whose exported values were later to undermine the system of imperial domination, the successors in the Soviet Union are a state bourgeoisie of managers, technicians, experts, who are given to the exercise of power, who value authoritarianism as a virtue, and who are without any sympathy for ideas of liberty and self-determination that might undermine their control. And whereas European, especially British, colonisers persuaded others as well as themselves of their racial and general superiority, the Russian as a 'racial' group appear to be regarded with contempt by most of the people they rule over in Europe.

Comecon

At the time that its forces ousted the Germans from Eastern Europe, the Soviet government began the process of subordinating the economies of these countries to its own. This was partly to exact war reparations but it soon became an institutionalised system of exploitation to the great benefit of the USSR and the great disadvantage of the states concerned, who, to add one injury to another, were prohibited from accepting American aid under the Marshall Plan. While the most directly exploitative arrangements were modified, comprehensive economic rationalisation was insti-

10 The East-West Strategic Balance

tuted in 1949 within what was called the Council for Mutual Economic Assistance (CMEA, or Comecon), a body for co-ordinating trade, currency, investment and production. But whereas the Warsaw Pact has never been invoked, except for the joint invasion of one of its members (Czechoslovakia), CMEA impinges directly and constantly on the economies and economic policies of the members. It gave rise after a few years of operation to resistance and divergencies of policy. While the Soviet Union can substantially determine the defence policies of its partners, it could only fully determine their economic policies if it could exercise day-to-day control in most parts and levels of government — a task beyond its capacities, especially as both the USSR and the East European states developed extensive economic relationships with the Western industrial powers. They looked to the West for capital and, in the case of Eastern Europe, technology geared to a consumerism which was deemed essential to contain political unrest. In the Soviet Union, consumer pressures are mainly in the towns, and have been easier to contain than, say, in Poland, where strikes in heavily-industrialised urban areas have periodically frightened and coerced the government. Despite the difficulties, the Soviet Union has always managed to maintain a significant economic hold on its European partners, differing only in degree.

This hold began at the end of World War II when the East Europeans were cut off from their traditional markets and suppliers in the West which were then supplanted by the Soviet Union. In important respects (but see Table 1), that dependence still remains.

Table 1 *Estimated Soviet and East European Currency Indebtedness to the West, 1979*

| | $US billion | |
	Gross	Net*
Bulgaria	4.5	3.7
Czechoslovakia	4.0	3.1
GDR	10.1	8.4
Hungary	8.0	7.3
Poland	21.0	20.0
Romania	7.0	6.7
USSR	17.2	10.2
CMEA banks	5.2	5.2
Total	77.1	64.7

* Net debt is gross debt less deposits with Western banks.

Source: CIA Research Paper ER80–10327, 'Estimating Soviet and East European Hard Currency Debts', June 1980.

Table 2 *USSR and Eastern Europe: Estimated Measures of Debt Burden*

	Debt service as a share of total revenues (Per cent)		Gross debt as a share of total revenues (Per cent)		Debt service as a share of loan drawings (Per cent)		Net transfer from West (Million US$)	
	1972	1979	1972	1979	1972	1979	1972	1979
Bulgaria	36	38	198	195	46	136	212	–233
Czechoslovakia	10	22	46	112	56	65	106	429
GDR	18	54	95	223	85	94	53	171
Hungary	14	37	140	239	37	131	243	–293
Poland	15	92	87	333	44	85	352	1 056
Romania	27	22	99	130	125	51	–68	1 130
USSR	14	18	68	64	52	168	432	–1 927

Source: CIA Research Paper ER80-10327, 'Estimating Soviet and East European Hard Currency Debts', June 1980.

Romania is a special case because of its oil production, its passion for independence and its political skills. President Ceausescu has managed to diversify his imports of strategic items. Romania became a net importer of oil in 1976, but looked first to the Middle East and only second to the Soviet Union. It is Romanian protest that has done most to prevent CMEA being turned into an outright supranational authority with the USSR the super nation. Poland is the only other member country with major developed energy resources, in its case coal, which, until 1980, made Poland a net exporter of energy. All the CMEA European members except Romania (Mongolia, Cuba and Vietnam are also members) depend on Soviet oil and natural gas, supplied in return for goods at price equivalents somewhat below world prices.[10] Soviet oil production (see Chapter 5) will be unable to meet increased bloc demands and on present indications only the Middle East can do so. By 1985, the volume of oil imported by East European states from the Middle East is expected to double to about 25–30 million tonnes — almost 25% of total imports which will have to be paid for in hard currency, a currency these states cannot presently earn from the Soviet Union.

The importance of bilateral trade with the USSR varies from country to country (see Table 3). It has the advantage of guaranteed markets. As East European states in the late 1960s and early 1970s increased their trading connections with the West, especially in machinery and equipment, their dependence on the Soviet Union declined, but in recent years Western economies hit by the oil price

Table 3   *Soviet Economic Relations with CMEA Countries: Eastern Europe, Imports of Selected Raw Materials from the Soviet Union as a Proportion of Domestic Consumption in 1977, in Per cent*

	Bulgaria	Czechoslovakia	GDR	Hungary	Poland	Romania
Crude Oil	93	95	100	88	90	—
Natural gas	100	89	30	16	27	—
Total energy	70	35	28	44	15	2
Cotton*	74	64	97	47	72	36

* 1976 figures

Source: *Energy Supplies in Eastern Europe: A Statistical Compilation*, CIA, 1979, OECD, *UN Statistical Yearbook*, *Soviet Agricultural Commodity Trade*, CIA, 1978.

rises became less able to import East European goods, while Western exports became more expensive. This has forced the East European back into a closer trading relationship with the USSR, which, as a country deficient in consumer goods, is able to absorb the sometimes uncompetitive East European industrial output (see Table 4). Eastern Europe has also been required to pay for its import of fuels and other raw materials from the USSR by the export of machinery and equipment, chemical products, food and other consumer items. The USSR, for example, takes 80% of Bulgaria's exports of textiles, fabrics, conveying and hoisting equipment, nearly 70% of Czechoslovakia's railway vehicle exports, and 90% of its non-electric power machinery. Partly by design, partly because of the global economic situation, much of Eastern Europe has thus become dependent on the supply of Soviet raw materials and ener-

Table 4   *Eastern Europe: Trade with the USSR as a Proportion of Total Trade (by Value) in Per cent*

	Exports			Imports		
	1970	1976	1977	1970	1976	1977
Bulgaria	54	54	54	52	54	57
Czechoslovakia	32	34	34	33	32	34
GDR	38	32	35	40	32	35
Hungary	34	30	31	33	27	27
Poland	35	30	32	38	25	29
Romania	28	18	19	26	17	19

Source: UN Monthly *Bulletin of Statistics*, June 1978 and June 1979.

gy. Yet the dependence is mutual, not least because of the Soviet Union's shortage of hard currency. It now depends on Eastern Europe for nearly 60% of its imports of machinery and equipment, and over 80% of imports of manufactured consumer goods. Soviet leverage derives from the greater size of its economy, the fact that what it obtains from its allies is less vital and often less internationally tradeworthy than what they obtain from the USSR, and to the inducements the USSR can give to the East Europeans to invest in Soviet industrial development the surplus income from their relatively uncompetitive exports (see Tables 5 and 6).

Table 5 *USSR: Balance of Trade with Eastern Europe, 1970–78, Million US$*

	1970	1971	1972	1973	1974	1975	1976	1977	1978
Bulgaria	−143	−112	−124	−125	+ 70	+178	+117	+223	+216
Czechoslovakia	− 31	+ 15	−144	− 69	− 10	+177	+130	+331	− 83
GDR	+201	− 13	−442	−340	+ 18	+467	+582	+808	+396
Hungary	+ 41	+113	− 91	−151	− 18	+ 58	+ 67	+145	− 49
Poland	+ 89	+ 72	−230	−148	+123	+ 57	+352	+440	−220
Romania	− 33	−92	−136	−124	− 45	−168	− 79	− 25	− 11
Total Eastern Europe	+124	− 17	−1167	−957	+138	+769	+1169	+1922	+249

Source: USSR trade handbooks.

Table 6 *The USSR's Importance as a Trading Partner for Eastern Europe in 1976, Per cent*

	Proportion of total imports supplied by the USSR		Proportion of total exports taken by the USSR	
Food	3	(1)	32	(11)
Fuels	68	(28)	15	(4)
Other raw materials	48	(12)	15	(2)
Chemicals	10	(2)	32	(7)
Machinery and equipment	22	(24)	43	(51)
Other manufactured goods	29	(20)	30	(24)

Source: UN *Bulletin of Statistics*, June 1978.

Note: Figures in parentheses show the proportion of Eastern Europe's total imports from and exports to the USSR accounted for by the individual categories.

In its attempts to make CMEA into a supranational economic organisation, the Soviet Union has tried to induce its partners to undertake standardisation of products and division of labour between them. On the whole this has not been very successful in practice, nor has the Soviet Union succeeded in obtaining better terms of trade between CMEA and the European Community and greater control of that trade. The East Europeans understandably want to make their own arrangements with their Western trading partners and creditors — creditors on whom both they and the Soviet Union depend (see Table 2).

Their economic difficulties have forced the East European governments to make changes in their systems of economic management in order to increase efficiency and the competitiveness of their exports. The criterion of profitability has reared its ugly head and become part of the scene almost everywhere. Further restructuring is required to reduce indebtedness to the West. The USSR has accepted this, hoping that it will not spill over into political attitudes. Yet how could it not do so? The Soviet economic model which they were for the most part obliged to adopt has proved inefficient and inadaptive. As the ultimate guarantor of the CMEA members' economies, the Soviet government has an interest in their viability. It was perhaps a perverse benefit for Soviet political imperialism that East European access to Western capital and technology, and the introduction of semi-capitalistic processes, ran into a global recession. The penalty of economic success might well have been, over time — and still might be — political instability, even a collapse of the system. As it is, the present trend is to a greater dependence, *faute de mieux*, on the USSR, except for Romania which has now signed an agreement with the European Community. Even the economy of the GDR, CMEA's shop window, is to be understood primarily as a part of the economy of the Soviet Union.

The Soviet situation

This is not the place to detail the changes that have taken place in Soviet society, government, economy and foreign policy since the second revolution in 1917 brought a communist government to power. From a vast, backward, semi-industrial country the Soviet Union has become one of the two military superpowers, the world's second largest economy, technologically advanced, universally literate, a heterogeneous but essentially unified state governed effectively if not efficiently by the oligarchy at the top of the comparatively small Communist Party of the Soviet Union. The traditionally intense nationalism of the Russian has been harnessed to a wider nationality and to a revolutionary ideology claiming to be superior to all others, universal in its application, and inevitable in its onward course.

The Soviet government faces a variety of internal problems which must affect its foreign and defence policies. It has never been able to adequately feed its population, and despite the cultivation of vast new areas in the east, it still imports many millions of tonnes of grain each year. The socialist (communist) system involves massive over-administration with no external constraints such as the market to direct and co-ordinate the components of production. A long-time emphasis on heavy industry has left the country perpetually short of consumer goods, adequate housing, transport and minor luxuries — it offers 'jam tomorrow' but very little jam today unless you are a member of the 'new class' of privileged citizens. With a declining birthrate and inefficient industries there are now labour shortages, relatively backward technology and poor productivity in some areas. The demographic trend also affects enlistments for the armed forces, and has aroused additional concern in that the non-Russian, non-European (Asian) part of the population is growing at a markedly faster rate, and by the end of the century the non-Russian element could be more than 50%. At a time when a number of Muslim countries are undergoing a revival of ideological fervour and want a greater temporal power for Islam, the Soviet government must fear the prospect of infection spreading to its 45 million Muslims.

Within the world's largest national land mass, the Soviet Union probably has the world's largest natural resources, but many of them are yet to be exploited and the extensive areas of swamp and permanent frost make extraction difficult and costly. Until recently it was believed that the USSR would run out of oil early in the twenty-first century (see Chapter 5), but there have been reports of new major discoveries and no doubt there are further undiscovered reserves on land or offshore.

We do not know what fundamental strategic considerations and foreign policy priorities are held in Moscow. Are they essentially offensive or defensive? All one can say is that they must be both, and that the evidence points to a strong offensive, expansionist or acquisitive element, which may itself have a defensive component. The Soviet Union is a continental power primarily concerned with the defence of the homeland and of the pervasive ideological regimen upon which the authority of the CPSU depends. It is a fortress state governed by fear and exclusion of alternative ideas. It has boundaries with 13 countries, including 10 000 kilometres with the Chinese People's Republic. Most of its larger non-Russian ethnic minorities live close to borders with other countries. Most of its exits to the open sea pass through waterways controlled by potentially hostile powers. Bulk transport between the eastern and western USSR depends on one long and vulnerable railway (see Chapter

6) or (for most of the year) much longer sea routes. There is no East-West road system.

The Soviet government and at least the Russian people are strongly conscious of their historical vulnerability to invasion and intervention, the most recent example being World War II when millions of Soviet citizens died. They have a sense of being encircled, and of facing possible threats from several directions. They are conscious of their proximity to potentially hostile forces in Europe, including American forces which could conceivably invade the Soviet Union whereas the Soviets are incapable of invading the US. They have grown up with a dogma equating capitalism with an inherently aggressive imperialism, and with the notion that military power is the essential basis of diplomacy and superior military power the only basis of security.

Soviet priorities would seem to be:

1   To defend the homeland and the Soviet system, and to extend and consolidate Soviet power and influence wherever opportunities occur.[11]

2   To maintain a relationship with the United States and other Western powers which prevents military confrontation between the superpowers, takes advantage of superior Western technology and food production, relatively and absolutely undermines Western economic and military strength, and divides and weakens the Western alliance.[12]

3   To preserve Soviet control of Eastern Europe and increase its influence in Western Europe. The 1975 Helsinki Final Act of the Conference on Security and Co-operation in Europe traded Western acceptance of post-war Soviet boundaries and territorial acquisitions for a Soviet commitment to human rights and to the reduction of tension in Europe through 'confidence-building measures'. While making some gestures towards the reduction of tension — gestures which would nevertheless maintain and legitimise Soviet conventional force superiority — the Soviets have quickly and brutally clamped down on human rights activists, as has also happened in Eastern Europe.

4   To undermine the power and influence of the Chinese People's Republic, both in the sense of reducing any Chinese threat to the eastern Soviet Union and in terms of defeating Chinese competition for ideological leadership and political status. The Russians have a long-standing fear of China, based partly on historical experience, partly on racialist fears, and also based on guilt over annexed territories, on the size of the Chinese population, the vulnerability of the Trans-Siberian Railway, and on China's limited but undoubted strategic nuclear capacity. The comparatively recent Chinese rap-

prochement with the West, especially with the United States and Japan, has greatly reinforced Soviet apprehensions.

5 To increase Soviet influence in the Third World, and to undermine that of the United States and China.

6 To provide themselves with the military power and global outreach to achieve these objectives.

The foreign policy of the USSR, like that of any other power, has to take into account the realities of power and the force of circumstances. It has gone through phases of expansion and consolidation. It has had its reverses, where neither military power nor militant ideology has been adequate. Although cast inflexibly in the terms of an ideological struggle between communism and capitalism, Soviet foreign and strategic policy is essentially about power and the will to exercise it. Soviet promotion of the concept of detente was not intended to result in a general relaxation of tension in which the USSR would participate. Its purposes were to create an atmosphere in which major arms control treaties and trade and technology agreements of benefit to the USSR could be negotiated and to weaken the confrontational will of the West, particularly in the Third World area of great-power competition.

At the same time, the Soviet Union has its own massive economic problems which, apart from economic reform, only the West can significantly alleviate. And the pressures and programmes for economic reform must contend with the interests of power and its systemic distribution.

This book is about policies and power, not about ideology. Milovan Djilas, first vice-president of post-war Yugoslavia, who was imprisoned many years for his unorthodoxy, brought the two together in a simple way in an article prior to the Soviet invasion of Afghanistan:

> The importance of ideology for the Soviet leadership — any Soviet leadership — is seldom understood in the West. For an American or an Englishman, 'imperialism' and 'expansionism' have to do with financial investment, technology, raw materials and the like.
>
> Not so for the Soviet leaders. Their rule is anchored in ideology, as the divine right of kings was in Christianity; and therefore their imperialism, too, has to be ideological or else it commands no legitimacy. This is why the men in the Kremlin can lose no territory once acquired, why they cannot abandon friends and allies, no matter how objectively burdensome they may have become to them . . . or admit alternative interpretations of the true faith.
>
> This is also why it is an unsupportable American hope that the Kremlin may be pressured or humoured into a type of comprehensive detente which would guarantee Soviet moderation in Africa or Asia as part of a SALT settlement, or any settlement. No Soviet leader can do that with-

out abdicating his title to leadership and jeopardising the justification of Soviet rule.[13]

As this goes to press, the Soviet Union is approaching, perhaps even undergoing, a change of leadership. The 'Brezhnev era' is drawing to a close. One can only speculate about the nature, timing and implications of change. A new generation of leaders must take over before long. This could occur gradually over several years, or it might happen quite quickly. Learning from Khrushchev, Brezhnev has deliberately not built up a possible succession of bright, younger men, and the Politburo, most of whose members were born before the end of World War I, seems almost incapable either of producing anyone other than a temporary replacement for Brezhnev or of throwing up acceptable younger leaders. If the old guard does manage to keep itself in power for long after Brezhnev departs, there could well be an explosion. The Central Committee of the CPSU is now largely dominated by regional secretaries in their fifties, whom Brezhnev, by apponting elderly cronies, has prevented from exercising real power. There are considerable frustrations also within the 'middle class' approximately 20% of the population who have been subjected to egalitarian wage policies. There are considerable pressures for economic reform along Hungarian lines. The new leadership will have to take account of these pressures and go some distance towards satisfying them, or there will be angry scenes and a reshuffle at the top.

What are the Brezhnev legacies, or the legacies of his period? One is the partial rehabilitation of Stalin and Stalinism, no longer commanding wholesale terror but too important a concept to be ignored. Brezhnev strengthened the primacy of the CPSU, reinforced conservative elements within it and brought back together its industrial and agricultural components — a separation on which Khrushchev had partially foundered. Defence, based on heavy industry, was re-emphasised, with agriculture third and consumer goods fourth. There has still been a general rise in living standards but nothing like the rise that could have occurred if consumer demands and desires had had a higher priority. And in the last years of the 70s, under the impact of massive defence expenditures and poor harvests, the overall rate of economic growth steadily slowed to an estimated 1–2%, with heavy borrowings from the West to provide adequate food, animal fodder and technology.

The shifting balance

Brezhnev has been generally identified with the policies of detente, and, at least until the Soviet invasion of Afghanistan, there was an apparent lightening in the atmosphere of East-West relations. Yet even in the area of the central balance, as affecting the USSR, Europe and North America, there emerged through detente a web of ambiguities with profits and losses difficult to evaluate and compare. The 'ostpolitik' of Willy Brandt found the USSR and, with Soviet consent, Eastern Europe coming to meet it. This diffused the rigidity of confrontation on both sides of the balance. On the other hand, especially in American minds, it aroused the possibility of the 'Finlandisation' of Western Europe.[13] It aroused in Poland and East Germany the fear that the USSR might do a deal with Bonn 'over their heads', as it were. It encouraged the two more liberal states of Eastern Europe, Poland and Hungary, to strengthen their links with the West. The prolonged talks on Mutual Balanced Force Reductions (MBFR) produced little in the way of force reductions or indeed of agreement on what the strength of those forces were. Only within the context of Helsinki did the Soviet Union make relatively significant, if still minor, concessions on the conduct of military maneouvres and the attendance of Western observers.[14]

On human rights, Soviet agreement to the wording of the Helsinki Final Act signed in late 1975, went far beyond any other formal Soviet commitment of this kind, and may have contributed to the considerable exodus of Soviet Jews. Yet in many respects the Brezhnev government, in defiance of Helsinki, has been more repressive of human rights activists than was its predecessor, thumbing its nose at Western opinion.

One can make a good case for the idea that at Helsinki as in other situations the Soviet government has traded on the West's attachment to the notion of good faith. By committing itself to social measures which (as seen from the West) it has no intention of fulfilling, the USSR obtained from the Western powers and from its own Warsaw Pact allies a legal recognition that they were expected to honour which relates to Soviet territorial aggrandisement as a result of World War II. Yet at Helsinki and at the follow-up conferences at Belgrade and Madrid, declared Soviet policies fed East European hopes and desires to attenuate the strict disciplines of bloc membership — fed the malaise that (as suggested earlier) seems bound eventually to topple the whole system as inevitably as the empires of Rome, Charlemagne, or their modern successors, were toppled — but (one must hope) in a shorter period.[15] The 'Brezhnev doctrine' of 1968, declaring in effect that socialist (communist) states had their sovereignty limited by membership of the bloc and were thus properly liable to Soviet intervention, is unlikely to have increased bloc fears (which were already considerable) of such intervention, but the incubus now hovered more menacingly over their sovereignty and independence.

While the Soviet empire, because of its vast military power, does not depend on active consent, it does depend on a degree of acquiescence. The East European leaders depend for their positions, even for their lives, on loyalty to the USSR. They are thus unlikely to give up such a loyalty irrespective of their personal feelings towards the Soviet Union. But just as in 1970 and 1980 the Polish people demonstrated that despite all the power of the state no leader is invulnerable, so, given enough simultaneous discontent in enough of the satellite states, will the Soviet Union eventually discover the limits to empire.

This is a 'feeling in the bones', but it is more than that, and more than wishful thinking. Europe is the cradle and nursery of nationalism, and despite the changes in borders and sovereignty that have occurred over the centuries, the independent sense and expression of nationalism in almost every European country, East and West, is a powerful and apparently unquenchable force. In addition to that, communism as a system has shown that it just does not 'deliver the goods', economically or psychologically, and it can be maintained in its various changing forms only by strongly repressive regimes the foundations of whose power lie in an imposed philosophy and an alien, external authority. Imposed philosophies are never permanent, and alien authority, if it remains alien, must eventually recede. Events in one East European country after another have shown the limits on Soviet power to avert or arrest change. Poland provides but the latest and the most significant example. It will not be the last. Soviet military power is unlikely to decline, absolutely or relatively, for a long time. East European states, when seeking freedom, may at times be at odds with each other. But Soviet capacity to enlist 'loyal' states to play off against rebellious ones has declined and will decline further. And although the Soviet Union may feel impelled to take desperate measures to prevent a disintegration that could rapidly infect its own homeland, if the history of Europe shows anything it shows that the time will come when there are no Soviet soldiers in the countries of Eastern Europe and no American soldiers in the West.

The Strategic Arms Limitations Talks (SALT) (see Chapter 3) offered constraints on the escalation of both Soviet and American nuclear weapons and expenditure, but did nothing to stop the Soviets from obtaining, as they have done, general parity with the Americans in nuclear arms and selective superiority.

Detente related to the central balance, leaving the marginal regions (as the USSR saw them) — the Third World — as areas for ideological, political and especially strategic competition. This was not understood by the US Congress during the Ford administration, nor by President Carter until America was shocked by the events of late 1979.

Soviet intervention in Afghanistan is not the equivalent of American intervention in Vietnam, but both were miscalculations that affected the strategic balance and reduced the capacity of the miscalculator to manage its alliance system.

Historically, Russia has been a continental power, expanding by military force across adjacent land frontiers. Until after World War II, the Soviet navy was an extension of continental defence, but its role, status and strategic purpose changed under the events of the Korean War (1950–52), the Suez War of 1956, and even more the humiliation of backing down over Cuba in October 1962. The Soviet leadership saw the value of being able to project naval power worldwide in support of political objectives as well as in competition with or emulation of Western navies (especially that of the US) with their growing nuclear strike capacities. From the late 1950s the Soviet navy began to move into the business of aircraft carriers, initially for anti-submarine warfare (ASW) with helicopters, and subsequently for fixed wing ASW and strike aircraft. A global navy required bases outside the USSR from which to operate.

In 1968 a squadron of the Soviet navy was placed in the Indian Ocean and given a permanent status there with access to Berbera in Somalia (until ejected in 1978), to the small facility at Hodeida in (North) Yemen and subsequently to the former British base at Aden in what had become the People's Democratic Republic of Yemen. The reasons for these developments may well have related to the American construction of facilities at Diego Garcia in the Indian Ocean and on the North West Cape in Western Australia, as well as to the US potential to deploy nuclear submarines in the Indian Ocean, but the effect was remarkably like that of the establishment of British coaling stations during the nineteenth century: to provide bases in the imperial communications chain, and in the case of the north-west Indian Ocean to give a capability to influence the strategic environment of the world's main oil-producing areas (see Chapter 5). A growing merchant marine and tanker fleet, aggressive mercantile shipping policies, and a large fishing fleet partly given over to intelligence-gathering, are part of a single maritime strategy that has caused some alarm in Western circles. Excessive alarm is premature, when one considers the size of other naval and merchant fleets and the fact that Soviet ships, like those of other nations, eventually wear out. Nevertheless a single maritime policy is a considerable strategic advantage and Warsaw Pact fleets are included under it. The Soviet navy is becoming an increasingly formidable fighting force, especially because of the continuing production of carriers, of a new class of battle cruisers, and a new class of attack submarines.

The final abdication and failure of American political and military policies in Vietnam in 1975 coincided with a shift in comparative power and intentions. The Soviet Union used its new intercontinental military airlift capacity to transport arms and thousands of Cuban troops to support the MPLA revolutionary regime in Angola. After the US Congress had refused Dr Kissinger the authority to intervene, Soviet naval and merchant shipping provided the protection and the supplies that maintained the MPLA in power. The Ethiopian revolution ejected the Americans from their positions of influence and from their communications station in Ethiopia and put Soviet advisers, arms and communications and Cuban forces in their place. Soviet naval facilities have subsequently been developed in Ethiopia's Dahlak archipelago in the Red Sea. The fall of the Shah of Iran and the expulsion of the Americans did not offer equivalent advantages to the USSR, but did offer comparative advantages. In Afghanistan, the communist coup of April 1978 ended what was left of American influence in that country and strengthened Soviet influence, which was further consolidated by the invasion of December 1979. In Vietnam, the USSR may have encouraged and certainly made possible the invasion of Kampuchea, which led to the Chinese attack on Vietnam in early 1979, which in turn ensured much more favoured access of Soviet naval shipping and military aircraft to bases in Vietnam, including former American base in South Vietnam (see Chapter 6). Here, the Soviet moves may have been related to the rapprochement between China and the United States and Japan, but the effect has been to give the Soviet air force a maritime reconnaissance capability throughout Southeast Asia, the south-west Pacific, and over most of Australia. It has potentially given an interception capability within part of that area and has given elements of the Soviet navy a greater flexibility in operations throughout the region.

For some years the USSR has been devoting a much higher proportion of its resources and effort to defence capacity than has the United States.* As a former senior member of the US National Security Council Staff wrote in 1979:

> There was no way around the fact that a consistent commitment at this general level for over more than a decade would not only pay off in the near term but would create a base for contining expansion. Leonid Brezhnev would leave his successors some major ambiguities in his dealings with the West, a legacy of bitterness and suspicion in his dealings

---

* The problems of comparing defence expenditures between countries are discussed in note 14 of Ch. 2.

with China, and a number of openings elsewhere that skilful Soviet handling might turn to permanent gains. But above all he would pass on an inheritance of military power unrivalled in Russian history since the days when the Czar strode into Paris at the end of the long march from Borodino.[16]

Will the new Tsars want to stride into Paris? There is no evidence to suggest such intentions, perhaps because they see no prospect of a safe opportunity to achieve them. But there is abundant, long-standing and continuing evidence to indicate that any foreseeable Soviet government will have a policy of military superiority over its non-communist neighbours, and of nothing less than parity of power with the West. The evidence also suggests that it will take advantage of Western political or military weaknesses to press for political and possibly territorial advantages; that it has a code of conduct akin to that of the European imperial states of the nineteenth century, inhibited somewhat by the complexities and norms of the present international system and by its own economic weaknesses, but reinforced by massive military strength, by a readiness to use such strength quickly and overwhelmingly, by a belief in ideological superiority, by the persistent practice of authoritarian processes of power, and by its capacity to enlist solid support from the Soviet public for its major foreign policy initiatives.

The alliance system by which the Soviet Union feels threatened, challenged or constrained had its origins in World War II: first, in the Anglo-American axis by which the War in the West and in Asia was won and the peace prosecuted; second, in the achievement of respectability in the American mind for the notion of alliances as being not disastrous entanglements but profitable or even essential partnerships in proper causes; third, in the major role which the United States, like some awakening giant, came to play in the conflict. Unlike all its enemies and all but one of its major allies, the United States ended the war at the height of its powers to that time, conscious of its superior international status and armed with unequalled physical and economic strength, the seductive machineries of diplomacy and a heady sense of moral virtue. When the Soviet Union took advantage of the disposition of its forces to create a form of empire in Eastern Europe, the United States was the only power willing and able to ensure that the new imperialism did not spread to the West European states so recently liberated from the tyranny of Hitler.

Having embarked on this crusade, reinforced by a domestic public opinion accustomed by history to populist politics and by the War to a passionate commitment to international peace and security, the American government took its sword to wherever the communist scourge appeared. It became the policeman of the world, and much of the world — physically and emotionally exhausted by the War — welcomed the event. Virtually wherever a nation was externally or internally threatened by communist forces the United States became its ally, willing (to quote President Kennedy) to 'pay any price, bear any burden' until the price and burden of Vietnam became out of all proportion to the effectiveness of the operation and the national interest it was intended to serve.

Thirty and more years after Europe appeared to become cemented into two opposing, mutually suspicious and hostile camps (where it still substantially remains) it is well to remember that the initial allied plans for the post-war recovery and security of the European states were only reoriented when it became clear to Britain, France and the US that there was much more to fear from the wartime Soviet ally than from the defeated German enemy. Over the period 1945–48, the Soviets abandoned any pretence to democratic principles, installed subordinate communist regimes in Eastern Europe and adopted obtuse and offensive tactics in occupation institutions. It supported communist insurgency in Greece, made territorial demands on Turkey, threats against Yugoslavia and refused for a time to evacuate occupied Iran; it also refused to cooperate in Europe's economic recovery, and blockaded Berlin. These were all formidable obstacles to a return to normality. It became evident that a return to normality, to a stable peace among independent European nations, was precisely what the Soviet Union did not want. The Truman Doctrine for Greece and Turkey, the Marshall Plan, the Brussels Treaty (Western European Union) and the North Atlantic Treaty together made possible the economic and psychological recovery of Western Europe as well as the reconciliation and interdependence of France and Germany within the evolving European communities.

North Atlantic Treaty

Under the North Atlantic Treaty, signed in Washington in April 1949, the member states[1] came to combine their military effort within a single organisaion (NATO) under a headquarters and regional sub-commands. Article 5 of the Treaty states:

> The Parties agree that an armed attack against one or more of them in Europe or North America shall be considered an attack against them all, and consequently they agree that, if such an armed attack occurs, each of them, in exercise of the right of individual or collective self-defence recognised by Article 51 of the Charter of the United Nations, will assist the Party or Parties so attacked by taking forthwith, individually and in concert with the other Parties, such action as it deems necessary, including the use of armed force, to restore and maintain the security of the North Atlantic area . . .

Like any other treaty, this one means what its members want it to mean at any given time. The wording allows complete freedom of action to members, from doing nothing to involving themselves in total war. But the commitments undertaken within the planning processes, the disposition of forces, the mutual interdependence — all make it more likely that the allies will act in concert in the event of a threat to any one of them. Between 1959 and 1968, France progressively withdrew from the formal military working of the alliance, but it still retains ground and air forces in Germany as part of the common defence, participates in NATO exercises, is represented in NATO agencies, and sits in the NATO Council and other 'political' parts of the structure.

The remarkable thing about the North Atlantic alliance is that it has remained relatively intact for all these years. Both NATO and the Warsaw Pact are held together by fear. In the latter case, so far as we can tell, while the Pact was brought into formal being because of German rearmament and participation in NATO, its driving force has been Soviet fear of American power deployed in Europe, of the possibility of another war with Germany, and fear that the ideas of national independence, capitalist democracy and individual liberty will subvert the East European states and remove them as a Soviet buffer against those ideas and against military attack. For Poland and Czechoslovakia, and possibly Hungary and Romania, there is fear of a reunified, 'revanchist' Germany on the one side, and of a powerful dominant and ruthless Soviet Union on the other. For East Germany there is the unequivocal fact of 19 occupying Soviet divisions, and there is fear of a populace disaffected by the adjacent presence of Germans with greater personal freedom, a higher standard of living, the television programmes beamed in — all the attractions that helped about three million East Germans to 'vote with their feet' and caused their government to put up a wall and an electrified fence protected by minefields, armed guards, and dogs to keep their own people in. It seems highly probable that if the populations of these states were able to choose both their governments and their foreign policies, they would choose very differently, but it will be some time and a different situation before any of them is given such an opportunity, a fact which speaks for itself.

Yet a Western observer cannot simultaneously look at the world, or at the strategic balance, with both Western and Soviet eyes, any more than a Muslim can see how human society, or 'truth', may look to a Christian. Various 'revisionist' interpretations of post-war history have been written, stressing the negative effects of American initiatives and justifying Soviet reactions. From Moscow, the Soviet Union appears 'encircled' and threatened by hostile powers, forces and bases. Thus in any attempt to reduce international tension, 'who started it' may be less important than current perceptions, intentions and capacities.

The NATO powers simply fear the Soviet Union's overt military power, repeated political threats and attempted subversion. Such is their individualism, their differences, their democratic reluctance to spend a cent more than is necessary on security, their preoccupation with all the non-security issues and situations of daily life, that they are reluctant allies, liable to divisions and squabbles. But fear of the Soviet Union keeps them allies nevertheless.

Western Europe

Since World War II, while the United States has had almost global preoccupations that expanded to meet the communist 'threat', the perspectives of the European imperial powers narrowed with the decline of empire, especially during the 1960s. There were legacies that survived — investment,[2] trade, security commitments, cultural inseminations — which led to British and French interventions in Africa, to concern with the Gulf, with Southeast Asia, Hong Kong, the South Pacific. But in recent years, in terms of the East-West balance, the West European powers have been mostly concerned with Europe. Here they face the potential enemy at first hand, across a line. If war comes, it seems certain that they will be in the firing line. They will suffer — as nations they may even *be* — the first casualties. Unlike the United States, by bitter experience repeated over the centuries they know what it is like to be laid waste by conquering armies. They have no desire to be laid waste by Soviet nuclear weapons. Before that happens, they want to have explored the alternatives, to be sure of the cause in which they risk destruction and to have some control over the negotiations and decisions.

The 30 years of NATO have seen the steady growth in quantity, range, explosive force, and precision of nuclear weapons by the superpowers and the development of modest but not irrelevant independent nuclear strike forces by Britain and France. The current strategic and tactical nuclear weapons equations are discussed in Chapters 3 and 4. NATO as an organisation began when nuclear weapons were still comparatively in their infancy. They were few in number. There were no nuclear missiles, no nuclear-powered nuclear-armed submarines. The Organisation has had to cope with the growth of Soviet weapons systems increasingly capable of devastating European and subsequently American centres of population. The ultimate control of comparable systems in the West had to be in the hands of the country that developed and produced them — the United States. The notion of a nuclear force with several 'fingers on the trigger' (a Multi-lateral Force, or MLF) was considered and discarded.

From the time when the Soviet Union could land nuclear-armed missiles onto the continental United States, European governments had to ask themselves whether or in what circumstances an American administration would risk that event by engaging in war in Europe, even in defence. The Federal Republic of Germany (FRG) had no alternative but to assume that the US would take such a risk to protect Western Europe against Soviet invasion. By agreement first with its European partners, then with the US, and for reasons of self-preservation, it could not and repeatedly said that it would not produce its own nuclear weapons. It could and did negotiate joint control over American nuclear weapons on German territory, although it cannot make the Americans use them.

For the small states of NATO it would be immensely costly to produce nuclear weapons and to continue to develop later versions. Britain, in at the beginning of nuclear weaponry, developed its own systems when the US Congress went back on the wartime agreement for sharing technology, but negotiated at Nassau in 1963 an agreement whereby it could incorporate more sophisticated American equipment, allocate the weapons to NATO but retain them for self-defence in a national emergency. Only France under de Gaulle felt able to go its own way in nuclear weapons. Piqued at the Anglo-American relationship and determined to be independent of an America she did not trust, France withdrew from the NATO integrated military structure, ejected NATO headquarters from French soil (it transferred to Brussels), and developed its own nuclear '*force de frappe*'. This France could do only because it was protected from conventional attack by its European partners (although France voluntarily contributed forces to the common defence), and from nuclear attack by the American strategic nuclear arsenal. Simultaneously de Gaulle arrested the institutional development of the EEC and prevented it from moving too far in the direction of a federation that France could not be sure of controlling.

Was the French anti-American withdrawal from NATO planning in effect also, as is sometimes suggested, withdrawal from an organisation in which the FRG was growing in strength and leadership? Despite the steps de Gaulle took to forge a Franco-German axis, his 'grand design' for France was within a 'Europe des patries' led by France. In the Community tough diplomacy could enable France to protect its economic interests, including a grossly inefficient agricultural sector. In NATO, which the United States dominated, diplomacy would not be enough, as M. Mitterand will discover.

The Federal Republic of Germany has gone through three stages since 1949. First, under Adenauer, it became integrated into the Western economic and security systems and adopted Western democratic political institutions and values. Second, under Brandt, it began the process of reconciliation, of learning to live with Eastern Europe and the Soviet Union ('ostpolitik') and persuaded the West Germans to accept the post-war boundaries of Europe. Third, under Schmidt, the economic resources of the country were brought to bear on foreign policy, and the Federal Republic came closer to being, psychologically although not militarily, an equal partner with the United States in the alliance system. The FRG wants good relations with the GDR but is not prepared to treat it like any other sovereign state.[3] This would run contrary to the FRG's Constitution, it would mean abandoning the Quadripartite Agreement over Berlin and thus affect Western capacity to control West Berlin (and access to it), and it would close off the option 'dear to most Germans' of reunification for Germany.

Ostpolitik, and a publicly more critical, less subservient attitude to Washington (as over the neutron bomb — see below, and the sale of civil nuclear technology to Brazil despite American protests) characterise the attitude of the present FRG government's changed view of its place in the world. It cannot do without the United States but it is not an American surrogate. It is conscious of its economic and political strength which give it a leading role in Western Europe. World War II is over, its iniquities are past, its generation of leaders gone. The time for shame, apologies and compensation is also gone. The new Germany wants to be accepted for what it is now. It resents American paternalism and American suspicions. If the United States could engage in detente, which is a form of ostpolitik, without arousing fears that it might make a deal behind its allies' backs, and if France from de Gaulle onwards could make overtures to Moscow, why could not the Federal Republic?

US interest in NATO

Rhetorically at least, there have been a number of phases of American policy towards Western Europe and the Soviet Union. Words such as 'containment', 'liberation', 'roll-back' and 'detente' have served American domestic politics and perhaps have represented states of mind or interest but they have not concealed the fact that the Soviet Union has been continuously adamant in retaining its authority over the satellite states. It has had the power to do so and has demonstrated that power through forcibly suppressing domestic unrest.

Whether or not the United States would 'commit suicide to defend Europe', it is clearly committed to the conventional defence of Western Europe through the several divisions of ground troops located there, plus air combat elements, and the families of armed forces personnel living nearby. These must be considered the tripwire of a larger American involvement. NATO planning involves the use of tactical nuclear weapons in the event of a Soviet breakthrough. Once tactical nuclear weapons are used, no-one can be sure of controlling the escalation process, and all talk of 'decoupling' the two is of uncertain value. Why then is the United States so heavily committed to the security of Western Europe?

There are no simple answers to questions of that kind. Rationally, one might say that without the American presence and guarantee, the European NATO partners could not hold out against Soviet military pressures and would quickly go the way of Eastern Europe or Finland. If this happened the United States would be heavily disadvantaged in its own global defence against the Russians. One might speak of the large quantity of US trade with and investment in Western Europe, or the links between Americans (largely migrants or the descendants of migrants from Europe) with their home countries, or the identification with Western values, beliefs and cultural history. All this is true but it is not the whole truth, which includes as well a sense of commitment, the continuing crusade against communism begun while American forces were occupying post-war Gemany, notions of honour and self-respect and the force of habit.

Any United States government must also consider whether the relaxation of military pressure against the Soviet Union in Europe might not free the latter for military adventures in other parts of the world. Conversely, since the early days of Vietnam, America's allies have been troubled by the fact that American concern with threats to its interests elsewhere may weaken the defence of Western Europe.

If the perceived threat to Western Europe, and the broad response through NATO, have been unambiguous, the alliance has had to deal with the multiple problems of a partnership of democratic states with changing leaderships responding to diverse internal and external pressures. In such circumstances, the continuity of the alliance is a tribute to the governments concerned, to the joint institutions developed, to Soviet power, and to the bellicose vulgarity of much of Soviet foreign policy — an iron fist in an iron glove.

One of the continuing problems of the Western alliance has been over defence procurement. Standardisation of arms, vehicles, communications systems, equipment etc., among the allies is so self-evidently desirable and indeed essential for effective defence. But this standardisation has not occurred to a significant extent. All but the smallest members have wanted the employment and other economic and technological benefits of defence industries. The larger states have pressed on with their well-established industries despite small markets. The United States has been reluctant to forego the profits from selling arms to its allies. They in turn have not wanted to be exclusively dependent on arms from any one state, and especially arms which, in a crisis, will need to be transported across the Atlantic. According to Hans-Peter Schwarz, in 1974 there were 23 different kinds of combat aircraft in NATO, 7 different groups of combat vehicles, 8 different groups of armoured personnel carriers and troop transport vehicles, 22 different anti-tank systems, 36 different models of radar guidance and targeting systems, 8 different ground-to-air missiles, 6 different classes of torpedo, and more than 20 different calibres in weapons up to 30 mm.[4] Some rationalisation has of course occurred, in the form of co-operation on development and production, production under licence, and local off-set schemes, but they still leave a hodge-podge of incompatible systems — incompatible, that is, *between* different national armed forces though less so *within* them.

Eurocommunism

The nature of Western democratic institutions has made possible the existence of a Trojan Horse, or of Trojan Horses, within the alliance: communist parties which are democratically represented in the various parliaments and potentially within government, yet which owe ideological allegiance in some degree to the Soviet Union. France, Italy and Spain* all have large communist parties, and for much of the 1970s they were notionally grouped together, a little simplistically, under the umbrella term of 'Eurocommunism'. NATO governments, and especially the United States, have been concerned as to what would happen to the state concerned, to its political orientation, its trustworthiness, its attitude to the alliance, if a communist government, or a government with the communist party as a coalition partner, came to power.[5]

There has now been a considerable amount written on this subject, of necessity largely speculation. When Dr Kissinger was Secretary of State, he declared that the United States would have to reconsider its attitude to NATO if communists entered government in a member country. The Carter government, after generously conceding that each member state was entitled to determine its own government, came to a conclusion similar to Kissinger's, if less forthrightly stated. The Reagan position is unlikely to be 'left' of Kissinger. There must still be some NATO secrets that have not been revealed to the Soviet government through its vast espionage network; and practical defence co-operation within NATO, and indeed the security of Western Europe, would suffer extensively and possibly irreparably if France or Italy were to become an ally of the Soviet Union.

But would this necessarily follow the election of a communist party into government? We can only get an indication from the actions and pronouncements of the three parties. All of them have demon-

---

* At time of writing Spain is not a member of NATO, but it is moving in that direction and is host to American military bases.

strated some independence from Moscow. All claim adherence to the constitutional road to power. All have said, at different times, that they do not propose to lead their countries into the Soviet bloc, although the French Communist Party (PCF) would like France right out of NATO. The PCF, which was for a time the largest opposition party, formed a 'union of the left' with the Socialist Party in 1972, a coalition that looked as if it might win the 1978 national elections. Whether from conviction or tactics, the PCF formally abandoned the 'dictatorship of the proletariat' in 1975 and moved away from the more extreme forms of revolutionary policy. But it left the coalition in 1977, perhaps under Soviet instructions, and probably for three reasons: the Socialists had become the dominant partner; Moscow was busy cultivating the French government and encouraging it to be as distant as possible from the United States; and if the coalition had won, it could not possibly have fulfilled its promises and would have been discredited. The PCF helped elect a Socialist president in May 1981, but Mitterand is unlikely to meet their demands and they may make trouble for him, for France, and for NATO.

The Communist Party of Italy (PCI) has been closest to power in that under its 'historic compromise' with the Christian Democrats it kept them in office for a time (1976–8) in order to get some PCI policies adopted. It is the second largest party in parliament. It withdrew support and forced an election when it felt the dividends did not justify the investment. The PCI lost votes in the last election. It is very conscious of the possibility of a right-wing backlash. It remembers Mussolini, drew a sharp lesson from Allende, and cannot but be aware of the extreme right-wing group gathering around the Italian Social Movement. It has said it is opposed to NATO in its present form, but would want to change it from within, not to leave it.

The Communist Party of Spain (PCE) is the smallest, the furthest from power and the strongest opponent of Soviet control. Its platform includes a peaceful, parliamentary transition to socialism (communism), the continued working of a multi-party system, and full civil liberties. The PCE leader, Santiago Carrillo, does not see the Soviet system as genuine socialism and does not acknowledge the Soviet Union as the leader of the communist movement.

The West European communist parties' public disavowal of Soviet infallibility, and their strong nationalist leanings, have not endeared them to the Soviet government, even though they have been encouraged by Yugoslavia and Romania. In the event of their taking office, would ideology take priority over nationalism?[6] Because they reject a violent road to power, this does not mean that they would eschew violence in holding on to power. The French and

Italian parties adhere to the concept of 'democratic centralism', to a one-party system of government. All three want to establish their legitimacy as communists. None could be expected to work against the general interests of the Soviet Union, nor to retain the support of their followers if they tried to do so.

The 1970s seemed to be the decade of Eurocommunism, witnessing its rise and decline — but this is too simple. In Italy, where unstable and corrupt government appears endemic and where the PCI has now 30% of the vote, the communist party is a formidable political entity with a generally good record in local administration. And if the rest of Western Europe and the United States, assisted by Soviet actions in Afghanistan, have been going through a more conservative phase, the one certainty is that it will not be permanent, as the French elections have demonstrated.

The southern flank

NATO was designed to protect Western Europe, but there was a great gap in anti-Soviet defences along the south-western borders of the Soviet Union. Britain, in the last flush of empire, stepped in to remedy the situation in 1955 by arranging a mutual defence agreement with Turkey, Iraq, Iran, and Pakistan. Originally known as the Baghdad Pact and, after Iraq's revolution and her withdrawal from the Pact in 1959, as the Central Treaty Organisation (CENTO), it had more psychological than material content. It did not carry the commitments of NATO with a multi-national force in being. Above all it lacked the formal participation of the United States, although the latter did have informal links with the Organisation. After the Iraqi revolution Iran turned for military aid to Washington, as did Pakistan directly and through the Southeast Asia Collective Defence Treaty (see below). CENTO gradually withered on the vine for lack of a defined threat, of common sentiment, and of adequate military power.

There was one other part of Southwest Asia whose security was guaranteed by Washington, although without a formal treaty, and that was Israel. Largely because of its Jewish population, the United States was prominent in the negotiations that produced the independent state of Irael and it subsequently provided most of the arms and much of the funds to sustain Israel during four wars with her Arab neighbours. Although not part of the anti-Soviet or anti-communist alliance system, the United States guarantee to the security of Israel was to affect subsequent US relationships with the Arab states and those states' relationships with the Soviet Union (see Chapter 5).

America's Asian alliances

Like the Soviet Union but unlike Western Europe, the United States looks out two ways onto the world — across the Atlantic and across the Pacific. It is one of the ironies of history and accidents of geography that the two American alliances systems, in Europe and in the Pacific, are based on the defeated enemy as principal partner. This was partly because new technology replaced much of their national capital destroyed by World War II, and because the national characteristics that had made them formidable powers in war made them formidable also in the post-war recovery.

The Soviet Union's understandable reluctance to enter the Far East war until it was effectively though not legally over, enabled the United States to manage, virtually on its own though with some support and criticism by British Commonwealth governments, Japan's transition to peace. Korea, a Japanese colony since 1910, was divided for occupation purposes between the Soviet Union in the North and the United States in the South, each instituting, before withdrawing, the form of government in which it believed. When in June 1950 North Korea, with the blessing of Stalin and Mao Tse-tung,[7] and a good supply of Soviet arms, attacked the South, it changed not only the situation in East Asia but it helped to solidify the West in its confrontation with 'communism'. Here, it seemed clear, was proof positive of communist aggressive intent. Here were the opening shots in a war of unpredictable dimensions. Here was the Soviet Union acting through a surrogate to expand its territory and power. The effect was to strengthen the Western powers in their anxieties and their determination (so that they established the military organisation of the North Atlantic Treaty) and to provide one of three bases for the creation of anti-communist alliances in East and Southeast Asia. The United States realised it had to move quickly to end the occupation of Japan, which it could no longer afford, sign a peace treaty which (contrary to the 1948 Constitution which had not envisaged the necessity) allowed Japan to defend itself and to become the base from which the United States could, if necessary, prevent further Soviet predations in Asia. The United States and Japan signed a Mutual Security Treaty in 1951;[8] the United States and the Republic of (South) Korea signed one in October 1953.

The proposed Japanese peace treaty alarmed Australia, still in the aftermath of its wartime apprehensions of Japan, and some astute Australian diplomacy combined with prompt participation alongside the US in Korea led to the Australia-New Zealand-United States Pact (ANZUS), the first collective security treaty in the Pacific. ANZUS was aimed less at defence against a rearmed Japan than against the forces of communism that had just taken over China and were stirring in Southeast Asia.

The second basis for an anti-communist alliance lay in the victory of the communist People's Liberation Army (PLA) in China and the escape of the rump of Chiang Kai-shek's Nationalist forces to the island of Taiwan. Although the Soviet Union had done little to help — and indeed a good deal to hinder — the Chinese communist operations, it quickly established supportive relations with the new government and in April 1950 it signed a 30-year treaty which, among other things, promised military help in the event of war with Japan or with a country allied to Japan (i.e. the US). The treaty only confirmed the view widely held in the West that aggressive communism was a single entity with its mainspring in Moscow and its agents everywhere.

The United States had supported Chiang in his war with Japan. Later, alarmed in Europe by Soviet aggressiveness, troubled by the 'godless materialism' of communist doctrine, and bemused by a romantic involvement with China since the beginning of the century, the US went on supporting him in his losing battle against the PLA, and was deeply hurt and offended when it was treated angrily by the communist victors. There was thus no basis for dialogue with them, whereas the dialogue with Chiang continued, and a military pact[9] guaranteed his security and supported his pretensions to be the government of China. When General MacArthur ordered United Nations (mainly American) forces to advance right up the Korean peninsula to the Chinese border, the United States found itself in effect at war with China, in a physical confrontation which cost many lives and from which it took four years to extract itself, as well as a psychological confrontation that lasted for nearly a quarter of a century.

The psychological confrontation lasted so long because of another semi-misapprehension in the West which the Chinese did little to remove: the notion that the communist insurgencies in East and Southeast Asia were primarily external, non-indigenous in their origin and strength and were being fuelled and directed from Moscow and Peking. It is true that the doctrines were imported, as indeed they had earlier been imported to Russia and China; that China and Russia had trained leaders and ideologues for the insurgencies, and provided in some cases a good deal of propaganda plus modest amounts of arms and cash. But the basic strength of each movement lay in the resentment against colonial control from which inequity and humiliation were believed to be derived, the simple appeal of a (largely misunderstood) communism as a messianic force and an elite doctrine offering its devotees national pride, economic justice and the exercise of power. Throughout Southeast Asia, from Burma to the Philippines and Indonesia, communists had been among the most fanatical, disciplined and effective fighters against the Japanese. When the coloured alien conquerors made way for the return of the white alien conquerors, the communists renewed their struggle, a struggle exacerbated and complicated by the fact that power was beginning to pass to their non-communist compatriots.

For the first few years after World War II, all this was not very visible, or if visible, not understandable to the white allies who had won the war or had it won for them by other allies, mainly white. France returned to control Indo-China; Britain to Malaya, Singapore, Borneo, and Hong Kong; the Netherlands and Portugal to their respective 'East Indies'; the United States, briefly, to the Philippines. The insurgencies began almost at once, but in different ways and with different strengths and effectiveness. Communists took little part in the armed struggle for independence in the Dutch East Indies. They had a much larger part in French Indo-China, and in Malaya the communists, racially Chinese almost to a man, constituted the armed struggle, fighting both the British and their own people.

Had these activities occurred in a world otherwise at peace, they might have provoked a very different reaction; but the world was not otherwise at peace. Much of it was in tumult, polarised between communist and anti-communist states and ideologies, between what were seen in the West as the forces of good and evil. The United States, which had disparaged France as a colonial power, now found her a vital ally in Europe and a besieged one in Asia. In 1954 Secretary of State Foster Dulles wanted America's allies to join in the defence of northern Vietnam, where for four years the insurgents had been supported by Chinese arms, but they refused. British Foreign Secretary Anthony Eden feared it would lead to 'the wrong war against the wrong man in the wrong place'.[10]

Having done everything they could within narrow limits to shore up the French position and having failed, after the 1954 Geneva Conference the Americans took over the defence of what was left of Indo-China. They managed to persuade seven other states to join with varying motives and degrees of enthusiasm in a collective treaty[11] to ensure if possible that the Vietnamese communists stayed north of the invisible and undefendable[12] 17th parallel of latitude. For all its many weaknesses the SEATO or Manila (where it was signed in September 1954) Treaty, or more particularly American commitments undertaken in the context of the Treaty, probably delayed the assumption of communist government over the states of Indo-China by about 20 years — years in which the world strategic situation changed, and changed most of all in eastern Asia.

It is conventional wisdom in retrospect to find nothing but fault with the American involvement in the Vietnam war, both in concept and in execution. Europeans saw the war as diverting to Asia the American effort which should properly have been used to defend Europeans. Undoubtedly the Americans made many mistakes, as they made many sacrifices. Their intentions were honourable: this was all part of the great crusade; it was to defend a country (or half a country) against communist engulfment. The war of course was not suddenly embarked upon; it developed over a period of more than a decade during which Soviet and Chinese arms and Chinese technicians poured into North Vietnam, a point many observers conveniently forget. It was in the middle of that decade (1960) that the Sino-Soviet partnership split rudely apart. One of the greatest tragedies of the post-war world was that no American administration, indeed no Western government, could leave its entrenched attitudes sufficiently to explore and perhaps take advantage of that division before several hundred thousand people had been killed in Vietnam.

The United States was not left wholly on its own to prosecute the anti-communist war in Southeast Asia, but from the mid-1950s it was almost alone. As with Korea, Japan properly opted out of all involvement except for basing American forces and making profits from defence industries. Britain was occupied with the insurgency in Malaya (1948–60) and the confrontation with Indonesia (1963–6). After Dien Bien Phu (May 1954), France wanted no part of the Indo-Chinese post-colonial situation, having an even nastier one to tidy up in Algeria. Pakistan was preoccupied with India. Australia and New Zealand contributed to the defence of the Malaysian archipelago, as they notionally continued to do after the British withdrawal. Australia, New Zealand, Thailand, the Philippines and South Korea made contributions in Vietnam. The Vietnamese themselves paid the major price of their externally-aided civil war. But of the non-Vietnamese it was the Americans above all who bore the burden, paid the costs, took the blame, and learned — too hardly and too late — the lessons. It withdrew its combat forces in 1971–2, reduced its aid thereafter, and South Vietnam was taken over by communist forces in 1975.

After that date the SEATO Treaty ceased to be relevant, except for the American and Australian commitment to Thailand which it included. Even so, under a doctrine enunciated by President Nixon at Guam in July 1969 and repeated to the US Congress the following February, the United States offered a nuclear shield to its allies in Asia, but insisted on their taking primary responsibility for their conventional defence. The United States retreated to lick its wounds and to seek by a more skilful diplomacy the total balance it could not achieve through shoring up fragile Asian allies in the way it shored up the Europeans.

Different priorities

Meanwhile, back in Europe . . .

To Europe, since the withdrawal of empire, the events of East Asia are rarely of major concern, even though interest in Japan as the world's third largest economic power and a participator in economic 'summit' meetings as well as a strong trading nation, does off-set to a degree Japan's low profile in international politics and its limited defence capacity. Strategically, China appears far more important, though essentially regional in its impact. No European can regret the fact that there are 46 Soviet divisions and a variety of missiles deployed against or near China and thus not available for use against Western Europe (see Chapter 6).

The relations between the two parts of Europe became far more complex over the years, and especially during the 1970s, than the single 'posture of gladiators' suggested by the opposing treaties. The GDR today is probably more hostile than the Soviet Union is to the Federal Republic; it does everything it can to denigrate, weaken or subvert its Western relation. Yet it also profits immensely from FRG credits and from the access to the European Community that the Federal Republic gives it. Trade is flourishing. The movement of families divided by the Wall fluctuates with East German imperatives. West Germany under Brandt and Schmidt and France under Giscard established a network of relationships with the East European governments. They were certainly not completely 'normal' relations as between fully independent states, but formally normal, as it were — much more normal than hitherto, and they took account of their varied interests and preoccupations. The fact that all the West European capitals except Bonn[13] sent teams to the Moscow Olympic Games is an indication of priorities which are not identical with those of the United States.

Their priorities are not identical for all the normal reasons of different national situations and for two further reasons: because the United States with its global interests and involvements can much more easily affect West European interests than Europe can affect America's; and because the West European governments have become uncertain about the competence of the American administration and about the wisdom of the West in allowing Washington to make its foreign policy.

Washington has always been the butt of European comments. A country which regularly elects or appoints a new team of amateurs as its head of state and government, its ministers, and its senior public servants, must expect some queries about their knowledge, sophistication and judgement. A nation as powerful and as pluralistic as the United States must expect some intellectual challenge from states who traditionally consider themselves naturally superior in wisdom and culture if (through no fault of their own) inferior in brute strength and bank balances.* But the current malaise goes beyond these bearable superficialities, beyond the resentment against aggressive US weapons acquisition policies.

One worry, exacerbated by the Carter administration, was whether the United States had the will, the capacity and the courage to continue to lead the Western world. This goes back partly to Vietnam, with its excesses of zeal and sacrifice in an uncertain cause and subsequent American disenchantment with the burdens of its world role. It also goes back to Watergate, to the political cynicism then displayed and the shame engendered. It involves (as outsiders see it) an American failure to react to Soviet expansionist policies, direct or through proxies, in Africa and the Middle East from 1974 onwards. It involves an unbalanced Middle East policy which in the long term may destroy the industries of the West through lack of oil. It also involves, so Europeans believe, a consistent American failure to understand Europe, to look at the world through European eyes.

In Carter's time, there were his pre-inaugural commitments to reduce defence spending,[14] and not to help Yugoslavia if it were attacked by the USSR. Both of these commitments were subsequently rescinded. Mr Carter's preoccupation with human rights questions seemed to prejudice more fundamental, life and death, issues. The delicate SALT II negotiations were thrown into disarray by new Carter initiatives, and they had not fully recovered when frozen by the Afghanistan war. In 1977 a Presidential Review Memorandum was leaked to the press which appeared to advocate

---

* In fact the EEC countries now have a combined gross national product well in excess of that of the United States. Americans thus may reasonably wonder why their NATO European partners cannot deploy total conventional forces of about the same size as the Americans', when the defence of Western Europe is the main issue at stake. The United States is quick to respond to any suggestion that European diplomacy is superior to that of the US by reminding its partners that for the past 30 years West European security has depended overwhelmingly on American military power, rather than on any West European native ingenuity. It is understandable that Americans complain that not only do West Europeans do little to help the general maintenance of security outside the NATO area, but even when dealing with the Soviet Union in Europe, the West Europeans want to carry the carrots while the Americans carry the sticks.

sacrificing about a third of West Germany in the event of a Soviet attack, to gain time. In 1978 President Carter persuaded several NATO partners, and especially the FRG, to accept deployment of enhanced radiation weapons (the neutron bomb), which were probably the best available defence against the Soviet tank threat, then he reversed his decision under pressure from a campaign mounted (among others) by the Soviet Union, and left the FRG's Chancellor hanging on to a sawn-off policy. In 1979, the United States revealed the existence of a Soviet combat brigade on Cuba and demanded its withdrawal. It is still there. In late 1979, when the USSR invaded Afghanistan, President Carter felt injured by Soviet deceit — an awakening seen in Europe as an astonishing piece of naiveté. By treating Turkey cavalierly, the US Congress weakened NATO's southern flank. The American dollar has been under constant attack, and not enough was done in its defence, to the detriment of Western financial stability, just as little has been done to bring in a sane energy policy. The USSR has been provided, by default, with a degree of nuclear superiority in the early 1980s, and former Secretary of State Kissinger (see Chapter 3) calmly told the West Europeans that the doctrine of protection by threat of an ultimate mutual assured destruction, on which they have based their strategy for 30 years, was 'absurd'.

For a long time the West Europeans watched with sympathy the patient shuttling of American officials between Israel and the Arab capitals, and breathed a common sigh of relief with the Begin-Sadat settlement. Yet the Carter administration appeared to see this almost as the end of the road rather than the beginning, unable — perhaps because 1980 was an election year — or unwilling to bring adequate pressure to bear on Begin to prevent his approving the settlements on the West Bank which must be a minefield to further negotiations and to a lasting peace. British and French proposals for steps towards a settlement of the Palestine question were coolly received in Washington. The Europeans have begun to exert themselves as a third force in the diplomacy of the strategic balance, as in the mission to the Middle East in August 1980 of the EEC's president-elect Gaston Thorn.

Two other issues troubled the alliance: the seizure of the American hostages in Tehran, and the Soviet invasion of Afghanistan. The former aroused European sympathies for the American position. Europeans viewed the latter also (but unreasonably) as primarily an American concern. It is unfair to see the failed hostage rescue attempt as a symbol of American decline, yet it did arouse such sentiments. The US pressure for European trade sanctions against Iran was understandable but put far more at risk in trade, investment and, above all, in oil supplies than the US itself was risking. And pressure for sanctions against the Soviet Union did the same in a different way, raising the possibility, for no practical effect, of undoing the patient gains of a decade in building links between the two Europes. As the West Germans said, 'Berlin is closer than Kabul.'

For its part, the United States has had its disappointments with its allies: in US eyes, they expect protection but are reluctant to pull their weight or give the support that would make American policies viable;[15] they find it difficult to agree among themselves; they are constantly lecturing Washington, constantly demanding. And there is the nagging US fear that the West German government, prodded by a wing of the Social Democratic Party and seduced by Soviet blandishments, might at some stage agree to trade neutrality for reunification. The Germans persistently deny this, and objectively it is hard to see any Soviet government promoting reunification of its declared enemy, or any West German government taking on the role of a Finland. An alliance without Germany and almost without France would be no alliance.

All these points merely confirm that the Western world is changing. There has been a decline in American leadership yet the West cannot do without American strength and there has been a rise in German strength but the West dare not (because of the fears it would arouse) accept too strong a German role. The West needs France and Germany in a roughly equal partnership, and the triumph of NATO and the EC is that they have produced that. It is too early in the Reagan administration, despite his rhetoric of firmness and strength, to see how it will shape up to leading the Western alliance and managing its relations with the Eastern bloc.

Soviet activities in black Africa, the Horn and the Yemens, the Indian Ocean, Afghanistan, Vietnam and Cuba will all be considered in subsequent chapters. They add up to a major, widespread challenge to American, and thus Western, power and influence. The US decision to build the MX missile, increase defence spending and bring in registration for the draft were the beginnings of a shift in the American mood to which Reagan's election has given a new thrust, and which may make the USSR pause while still allowing America's allies to insulate detente along the central front from turbulence at the periphery — to rethink their politics without reducing their cohesion.

It could be said that surely, after all these years, the Western powers ought to be able to look to a continued relaxation of tension with the ultimate goal being the removal of all foreign forces from the countries of Europe. May it be, as some observers claim, that the Soviet Union is understandably obsessed with its defence and that a much less heavily-armed Western Europe, a Western Europe, unable to attack eastwards, would enable the Russians to phase out their own forces and leave Europe at peace? Unfortunately there is nothing in the philosophy or actions of the Soviet government to support such a thesis. Soviet bloc propaganda consistently points to the burial of the capitalist West and its absorption into a communist system. Soviet domestic philosophy rests on assumptions about the nature of the system which both preclude independent thought and action and require the steady expansion of the regime's authority. It is a fundamental principle much quoted in the Soviet press that, 'It is the duty and aim of the Soviet government and party to improve the correlation of forces in the world in favour of the forces of peace and socialism' (i.e. of the Soviet Union), and nothing once gained for 'peace and socialism' is to be given up. Soviet armed forces in Europe are not as great, as well equipped or as well trained as they are often portrayed, but they are still far greater than are required for the defence of the Soviet Union. Soviet deployment of the SS-20 missiles (see Chapter 4) for use against Western Europe (which are apparently invulnerable because of their mobility) offers a new level of intimidation to the Europeans, both physically and politically. Will the United States be able to counter that vulnerability, to mobilise NATO out of its intimidation? The trend of the overall defence capacity of the USSR is towards steadily larger forces capable of being used in increasing numbers and kinds of situations on a global basis. And in the Mutual Balanced Force Reduction (MBFR) talks in Europe the only set of negotiations seriously devoted to disarmament, which were conceived over a quarter of a century ago by the Polish Foreign Minister Adam Rapacki and set in motion by NATO's Secretary-General Manlio Brozio, the opposing sides have not yet been able to agree even on a data base from which to begin. The Soviet Union is obsessed with secrecy about its military capacities, a secrecy without which it would feel naked and vulnerable to the world, a secrecy with which, it seems clear, no profitable arms reductions can be negotiated. Until they are negotiated, no Western government will feel able to dispense with the alliance system guaranteed by the United States and sustained by common endeavour.

3   THE SOVIET-AMERICAN NUCLEAR CONFRONTATION

An intercontinental nuclear confrontation has existed for nearly 30 years, since the Soviet Union developed heavy bombers and then intercontinental ballistic missiles (ICBMs) with nuclear warheads capable of reaching the United States.

Once the USSR could hit targets on the American mainland it became an objective of both states to be able to launch unacceptable retaliation after receipt of a 'first strike'. The processes of weapons development and testing and negotiation on arms control since that time have had additional, and somewhat different, objectives for the two states: in brief, for the United States to stabilise the competition under conditions of mutually assured destruction at levels that could be called parity but which in fact demonstrated American superiority; for the Soviet Union to obtain at least parity with American intercontinental capacity and to prevent West Germany from having access to such weapons; for both states to take maximum diplomatic advantage of their nuclear weapons and to keep a rein on economic expenditure on them. Both states have assumed a degree of stability in the nuclear balance and have looked for ways to maintain that stability at a lower cost.

The current strategic nuclear debate in the West is largely on whether, or in what ways, the United States can be expected to have the capacity and will during most of the 1980s to launch a second strike credible to its friends and allies, without provoking a counter-retaliation by the USSR of totally unacceptable magnitude. The question of credibility is important, because there is no way of being certain, in advance, of the outcome of a nuclear war.

The present state of the strategic nuclear balance is a complex one and the actual details, even from the best available sources, have ambiguities and disparities. Simple figures of numbers of weapons give an inadequate basis for any precise comparison, as they do take into account the pay-load of the missile ('throw-weight'), the explosive yield (in terms of equivalent tonnage of TNT), the accuracy of the weapons, or their degree of protection from pre-emptive attack. Most Soviet ICBMs, for example, have a greater throw-weight and yield than the US ones and the latest Soviet missiles have a reported accuracy approaching the best US missiles, i.e. to within about 200 metres. With multiple independently targetable re-entry vehicles (MIRVs) which have several warheads each capable of finding and attacking a different target, the number of launchers (themselves targets for the opposition) per warhead is reduced. On land where they are visible this is a clear offensive advantage but may be (except where they are mobile) a defensive disadvantage in that fewer enemy missiles are required to destroy them in a first strike. At sea, where they are still immensely difficult to discover, the MIRV enables more missiles to be launched from fewer needless in the haystack, as it were, although so advanced is US anti-submarine surveillance technology that it is understood to keep a close tab on most Soviet nuclear submarines, at least in the Atlantic. The 950 Soviet submarine-launched ballistic missiles (SLBMs) are carried in 64 submarines, the 656 US SLBMs are in 41 submarines. Five Polaris SSBNs were scheduled to be withdrawn from the US force in financial year (FY) 1980, and another five in FY 1981. Two new Trident submarines with 48 SLBMs are to be introduced concurrently, giving the following total SLBM force in 1981:[1] 320 Poseidon SLBMs on 20 Poseidon submarines; 176 Trident SLBMs on 11 Poseidon submarines; 48 Trident SLBMs on 2 Trident submarines.

Missile gaps or windows

At different times over the years critics of the US government have pointed to a US 'missile gap', i.e. an alleged Soviet superiority in intercontinental missile capacity. These 'gaps' have quickly disappeared either because they were imaginary in the first place or because of new American technology. The belief in a coming 'gap' or 'window of opportunity' has been widely held, not only in the United States but also in much of Europe and elsewhere. The notion of a 'window' means more than a simple superiority in one form of warfare, but a conjunction of circumstances providing for a period a superior capacity to destroy land-based missile silos and conferring an appropriate opportunity to take advantage of that superiority in a 'first strike'. It is widely held that the progressive installation by the Soviet Union of SS-18 and SS-19 ICBMs with a large number of MIRVs (up to 10) will by about the mid-1980s give the USSR, at least in theory, the capacity to destroy about 90% of American ICBMs in their silos. Allowing for inaccuracies, countermeasures and 'fratricide' of missiles,[2] the proportion of US missiles destroyed must drop (it is said) to less than that figure, and if they were launched on warning (see below) it would be very much lower. In fact present US estimates are that the Soviets could destroy 500–600 US ICBMs in 1981, and up to 900 by 1985. The point is that the United States in recent years has coasted along with its ICBM deployment, its most modern missiles being the Minuteman III which began to be operational in 1970.[3] During the intervening period, the USSR has brought into operation the SS-17, SS-18, and SS-19 missiles, and currently has five new or improved missiles under development. By upgrading the deployed (and mobile) SS-20s to SS-16s (of which the SS-20 comprises the first two of three stages) the Soviet Union could achieve a mobile ICBM capacity, if not prevented from doing so by SALT II or its successors, and provided some limitations on the SS-16 were overcome.

The Soviet missiles' size, accuracy, number, and number of warheads have caught the United States less than fully prepared. Some of the SS-18s have 8, 10 or (reportedly) 14 re-entry vehicles, and some of the SS-19s apparently can take six. Single warhead SS-18s have an 18-25 megaton warhead — enormous destructive capacity, and the SS-19 a 5-megaton. The Soviet Union thus has several thousand nuclear warheads from land-based missiles capable of release against 1 054 American ICBM silos, plus 950 from submarines (see Table 7). Despite the increasing sophistication of SLBMs these still do not have the accuracy for assured destruction of 'hardened' (i.e. heavily protected by concrete etc.) missile sites, or 'silos', but all of these missiles can, of course, also be used against other military installations, industrial areas, centres of communications, or populations.

The difference developing between the Soviet and American strategic nuclear capacities (see Tables 7 and 8) lies in the greater Soviet ability to destroy ICBM sites. The United States, even with its MRVs and MIRVs, has less than half the number deployed by the USSR (2104 compared with 5058).[4] This is still enough, at least in theory, to immobilise Soviet ICBMs in a first strike, but few people believe the US would in fact strike first even though it has not renounced the possibility. It is proceeding with developing the MX missile, a new generation of ICBM capable of being moved around and thus much less easily targeted. The Carter administration planned for 10 MX missiles to be deployed by 1986 (the full 200 to be deployed by 1989) in a set of mobile sites, proposed as a kind of race track with a series of shelters. Under President Reagan, the MX has assumed greater urgency and is being developed on a different basis of deployment still to be revealed.

Soviet ICBMs would take approximately half an hour to reach targets in the United State. If those targets are American ICBMs, the latter would need to be launched within that period or face the risk of destruction. This response is known as 'launching under attack', or — from the time a warning is received — 'launch on warning'. Although the technical capability to launch within the

Table 7   *US and Soviet Strategic Nuclear Weapons, as at Mid-1980***

Types	United States			Soviet Union		
	Single Warhead	MIRVed	Total	Single Warhead	MIRVed	Total
ICBMs						
Single Warhead	504			790 (d)		
MIRVed		550 (a)			608	
Total			1054			1398
SLBMs						
Single Warhead				843 (e)		
MIRVed		656 (b)			160	
Total			656 (c)			1003 (f)
STRATEGIC BOMBERS						
Single Warhead	381 (g)			156		
Total			381			156
Totals	885	1206	2091	1789	768	2557

* Based on the IISS *Military Balance* 1980–81; the 1980 White Paper, *The Security of the Federal Republic of Germany and the Development of the Federal Armed Forces*; the United States Joint Chiefs of Staff *Military Posture for FY 1981*; and UK *Defence in the 1980s*. Statement on the Defence Estimates 1980, Vol. 1, 1980, (cmnd 7826).

Notes: (a) Each with 3RVs. (b) *The Military Balance* states that 160 Polaris A3 missiles have 3 MRVs, 448 *Poseidon* C3 missiles have 10 MIRVs, and 48 *Trident* C4 missiles have 8. (c) US *Military Posture* states that there are currently 41 SSBNs of which 10 are equipped with Polaris A-3 SLBMs, 30 with Poseidon C-3 missiles, 1 with Trident-1 (C-4) missiles. The Trident of *Ohio* class SSBN is in production, 6 being scheduled for deployment between FY 1981 and FY 1985, equipped initially with the Trident-1 or C-4 missile capable of carrying 8RVs to a range of 7 500 km. The C-4 is being backfitted into 11 Poseidon SSBNs. Of the 10 Polaris SSBNs being withdrawn, 2 are being phased out and 8 converted to attack submarines. (d) Later models of some of these missiles (SS-11 and 13) have been equipped with 3 MRVs. (e) Comprises SS-N-5, 6 and 8 and SS-NX-17s. Some models of the SS-N-6 have 2 MRVs. (f) *The Military Balance* total of 1 003 includes 60 SS-N-5s (range 960 km) which because of their range are not included in SALT II totals. New missiles coming into service have 3RVs. (g) *Military Posture* for FY 1981 (p. 42) states that current planning is for 348 B-52s to remain in the total active inventory into the next century, plus FB-111s of which 66 remain in the active inventory. Some 30 per cent of the strategic bomber force is ready for immediate launch at all times. *The Military Balance* figure comprises 316 B52s (D, G and H) and 65 FB-111As. The US also has 254 carrier-based aircraft capable of dropping bombs on the Soviet Union.

Table 7a   *SALT II Maximum Number of Nuclear Weapons Allowed to Superpowers*

Until 31 December 1981	2 400 weapons
After 31 December 1981	2 250 weapons
of which	1 320 may be MIRVed
of which	1 200 may be MIRVed ballistic missiles
of which	820 may be ICBM launchers

warning time probably exists, the combined technical and political processes of making and implementing a decision would normally take considerably more than half an hour, especially if the Soviet missiles came without any prior build-up of political and military tension. That is extremely unlikely, although not completely inconceivable. It is much more probable that any decision to launch a nuclear strike, if it ever occurred, would be the culmination of a process of political confrontation and military build-up, even of conventional warfare. Neither government is going to leap lightly into a holocaust. The 'strategic warning' thus achieved would almost certainly entail preparations on both sides for rapidly implementing a nuclear decision once taken. At present American nuclear forces are on a far higher degree of alert than Soviet forces presumably because the Americans fear a surprise Soviet attack while the Soviets do not fear a surprise American attack.

The Soviet strategic nuclear force is comprised of ICBMs, and SLBMs. Strategic bombers, 113 Tu-95 *Bears* and 43 Mya-4 *Bisons*,[5] introduced into service in 1956, have a range of some 10 400 km and 9 600 km respectively, but are very vulnerable to interdiction and are not usually considered a credible intercontinental weapon. The *Bisons* are being phased out, but a new medium-range bomber, the Tu-22M *Backfire* with a range of up to about 8 000 km[6] is being deployed. With in-flight refuelling, the range of the *Backfire* is increased by about 40%. In the SALT II agreement signed at Vienna in June 1979 but not ratified by the United States, the Soviet Union, by an unsigned attached letter, undertook not to use the *Backfire* as a strategic (i.e. intercontinental) nuclear delivery vehicle, to limit the numbers to be fitted with in-flight refuelling capacity, and to restrict production to a maximum of 30 per year. *Backfire* is a highly sophisticated aircraft, and as the United States is less well prepared than the USSR for anti-aircraft defence, if the USSR reversed its position *Backfire* could be a highly dangerous weapon, as indeed it is considered in Western Europe. In any case, no reversal may be necessary, as there are strong and persistent rumours that the USSR is building a new long-range strategic bomber.

For the United States, bombers are an inherent part of the defence 'triad', along with ICBMs and SLBMs. Most of the bombers are B52s, with a range of 16 000–21 000 km, an old and relatively vulnerable aircraft but still extremely useful in a stand-off role (i.e. carrying cruise missiles), or in a follow-up to a missile attack. They are capable of attacking and destroying ICBM sites provided they get through the defences. There are also 170 medium-range Fllls (type E and F) with a range of about 4 800 km located in Britain, and 66FB llls in the US. These at present have a good chance of penetrating Soviet anti-aircraft defences. They are not counted as 'strategic' systems under SALT.

Although it voluntarily lagged in ICBM development, the United States is ahead of the Soviet Union with a different technology, that of cruise missiles (pilotless aircraft), defined in the SALT II Agreement, Article II (8), as unmanned, self-propelled, guided, weapon-delivery vehicles which sustain flight through the use of aerodynamic lift over most of their flight path'. First developed by the Germans in World War II and then largely neglected, these have been greatly improved in recent years, with a reported capacity for accurate (to a few metres) delivery over short or long distances. They can be launched from the ground (GLCMs), from ships (SLCMs) or from aircraft (ALCMs). They are much slower than ballistic missiles but are much smaller and are capable of flying close to the ground and so can more easily penetrate defences than can the bombers that carry them and fire them from a distance. Both the Soviets and the Americans have short-range ALCM, but the United States is further ahead in the development of a long-range (2 400 km) missile, which should be in operation with one squadron of B52s by late 1982, although problems in development have been reported. By 1985, when the originally agreed SALT II (if ratified) would be due to expire, there should be 120 B52Gs fitted to take ALCMs. A B52G is capable of carrying 20 ALCMs, but will probably carry 12, plus 6–8 short-range attack missiles (SRAMSs) for self-defence. There are different expert views as to how effective ALCMs would be against hardened ICBM sites, and whether, in view of their comparative slowness, the Soviet government would have left missiles in silos waiting for the ALCMs to arrive.

Under the SALT II Protocol (see below), the deployment of GLCMs and SLCMs of a range of more than 600 km would be prohibited, (Article II (1)) at least until 31 December 1981, although the treaty (Article IV (14)) and attached statement) allows testing or deployment of long-range cruise missiles from bomber aircraft up to a maximum of 20 per aircraft. Each bomber so equipped counts as a MIRVed weapon in the SALT tally.

This brings us back to the question of whether a 'window of opportunity' for the Soviet Union exists, or will exist, bearing in mind that a lot of people, including eminent Americans such as Henry Kissinger, say that they believe it does or shortly will exist, and even President Carter's Secretary of Defence Harold Brown acknowledged to the US Senate on 19 September 1979 that 'the problem of ICBM vulnerability is real and requires solution'.

A key aspect to the 'window' concept is the thesis that if the US land-based ICBM force is destroyed in a Soviet first strike, the American president will have to decide whether to respond by the use of SLBMs, whose accuracy is less than the ICBMs and which therefore are of limited use in a 'counter-force' role, against Soviet missile sites, and must be used in a 'counter-value' role, against Soviet cities, industrial centres, etc..

To do the latter would presumably involve immediate retaliation against American cities and therefore a president under the threat of a Soviet ICBM strike is faced with the dilemma of national surrender or national suicide.

Dr Brown in his Senate testimony called this a 'false dichotomy', a 'false dilemma':

> Even under the most pessimistic scenario, the United States would have several thousand surviving warheads including our remaining submarine, bomber and cruise missile, and even our depleted ICBM force [assuming not all would be destroyed]. These would allow us a number of counter-military, counter-industrial and urban options, not just a massive attack on population centres. We could, for instance, target remaining Soviet strategic forces, theatre nuclear and conventional military targets, and selected industrial and control targets in reprisal and still have sufficient warheads in reserve to deter a counter-city exchange.[7]

On the estimates given above, (a) the ALCMs will not be deployed in sizable numbers until about 1985, and they would need to be, in order to make effective, saturation counter-force and counter-value attacks on important Soviet targets and their defences;[8] and (b) it will be about 1985 (though perhaps earlier) before enough SS-18s and SS-19s will be deployed to destroy 90% of US ICBMs. By 1985 or a little later the US should have deployed new SLBMs on Trident submarines, with improved counter-force capabilities. If these steps are taken, the 'window' will not be as transparent as it has been described.

Imperfect knowledge

Yet we are dealing with a variety of imponderables. The US ALCMs are not yet in service. They may turn out to be far less effective than currently believed. The Soviets are bound to be developing defences against them. No nuclear weapon has ever been used or tested against a defended target. It is not known how effective electronic counter-measures or counter-counter-measures will be. New Soviet weapons may be close to deployment. While new discoveries now by the scientists on either side will be unlikely to affect the balance for several years, decisions by either government — based on their perceptions or misperceptions, their emotional reactions, their determination or lack of it — could well do so, and it is reasonable to assume that both governments will change during the period. Both governments also are susceptible to pressures from their constituencies, and although the real constituency of the Soviet government is very much smaller, more homogeneous and much more biddable than the American, it has its own dissensions and unpredictabilities.

From the time of the first Nixon administration, the United States began to examine options for the use of nuclear weapons short of the massive destruction of Soviet cities and installations. The 'counter-force' doctrine of Secretary of Defence James Schlesinger was refurbished and restated in 1979 under Mr Carter's Presidential Directive 59 which provided for a variety of possible nuclear actions in the event of a decision to use nuclear weapons, either as first or second strike. This had always been possible, even if it had not always been accepted doctrine.

SALT

The Strategic Arms Limitation Talks (SALT) which began informally in 1967 and formally in 1969 marked a recognition by the United States that the Soviet Union was approaching parity with it in strategic nuclear weapons, and that competitive escalation was in the interest of neither power. The 1972 treaties collectively known as SALT I consisted essentially of two agreements: (a) the Anti-Ballistic Missile (ABM) Treaty which indefinitely restricted to a small number the deployment by both sides of anti-ballistic missile systems (or anti-missile missiles); and (b) an Interim Agreement to freeze for five years the number of offensive strategic ballistic missile launchers to the number then deployed or under construction in each country. Subsequent negotiations for a more permanent arrangement were not completed within the five years, but with some accepted variations the second agreement was continued to the time when (it was assumed) a more permanent agreement (SALT II) would come into force.

The SALT II negotiations continued for seven years, and were concluded when President Carter and Chairman Brezhnev signed the Treaty between the United States and the Union of Soviet Socialist Republics on the Limitation of Strategic Offensive Arms at Vienna on 18 June 1979. A complex document with a protocol and a series of attached 'understandings' and statements, the SALT II Treaty, if implemented, would have the following essential features:

1 Both nations would be restricted to a total of 2 400 strategic nuclear delivery vehicles until 1 January 1981 and to 2 250 thereafter[9] until the end of the Treaty (31 December 1985). (This therefore would require the Soviet Union to dismantle some existing delivery vehicles.) Of the 2 250, 1 320 (including bombers equipped with ALCM in excess of 600 km) may be equipped with MIRVs. Of the 1 320, 1 200 may be ballistic missiles. Of that 1 200, no more than 820 may be ICBMs.
2 The construction of additional ICBM launchers would be prohibited, and neither state would be permitted to increase the number of fixed launchers for heavy ICBMs. (This would give the Soviet Union a continuing preponderance in heavy ICBMs.)
3 The number of warheads on currently existing types of ICBM would be frozen at existing levels. (This would restrain the Soviet Union from increasing the number of MIRVs on its heavy ICBMs.) SLBMs would be limited to 14 warheads.
4 Each country would be permitted to *test and deploy* only one new type of light ICBM for the duration of the Treaty. (This would entitle the US to proceed with the MX, but would restrict the Soviet Union to deploying only one of the several new weapons currently under development although it may *upgrade* existing weapons — a blurred distinction. The MX, if produced, will probably carry the maximum permitted number of 10 warheads and will have three times the throw-weight of the Minuteman.[10])
5 The average number of cruise missiles carried on heavy bombers is limited to 28 (there is a limit of 20 on present bombers such as the B52).
6 There are various provisions designed to make it easier for each side to check whether the other is adhering to the Treaty.

Under the *Protocol* to the Treaty, which would expire (unless renewed) on 31 December 1981:

1 The deployment of mobile ICBM launchers and flight testing of ICBMs from them are prohibited.
2 The flight testing and deployment of air-to-surface ballistic missiles are banned.
3 The deployment of ground-launched and sea-launched cruise missiles (GLCMs and SLCMs) is limited to cruise missiles with a range of not more than 600 km. (There is nothing to prevent long-range

cruise missiles from being developed during the period of the *Protocol*, and the US is in fact doing so. The USSR has a number of cruise missiles with a range of more than 600 km.)

So far, both the US and the USSR have acted as though SALT II were in operation. This seems likely to continue until completion of the new negotiations by the Reagan administration.

If the Treaty or something close to it is ratified, if its provisions are adhered to, if the *Protocol* is not extended beyond 1981, and if the calculations of weapons capacity are correct, the two sides should still have a rough overall parity in strategic nuclear weapons.

But these are very big 'ifs' and until December 1979 they lay at the heart of the American debate over SALT II. The oponents of the Treaty took one or more of the following positions:

1 SALT II confirms Soviet strategic nuclear superiority especially in the area of heavy nuclear weapons, yet the United States has denied itself the option to redress the balance. (On the other hand, the US had more than enough other nuclear capacity to deter Soviet use of its heavy weapons.)

2 Despite official and officially-inspired claims to the contrary, the United States is unable to verify key aspects of the Soviet strategic nuclear programme. The National Technical Means (NTM) for verification include photographic satellites, electronic systems located on ships, aircraft and ground stations that collect Soviet technical data transmitted during tests, as well as other forms of intelligence. Immensely sophisticated and comprehensive though these are, they do not tell the United States *how much it does not know*, so closed and secretive is the Soviet system. The monitoring capacity lost through the Iranian revolution has not yet been fully recouped. There are published suggestions that the Soviet Union 'cheated' on SALT I,[11] just as it had been patently untruthful over the question of missiles on Cuba. In breach of SALT II it *could*, if it so decided, with almost no risk of detection, circumvent throw-weight restrictions; it could place MIRVs on existing single-warhead ICBMs or SLBMs; it could mount an excessive number of long-range cruise missiles on bombers; it could provide in-flight refuelling for the *Backfire* bombers; and it could deploy ICBMs such as the SS-16.[12] (While there is some truth in these arguments, US capacity to detect or verify Soviet nuclear capacities by scientific means is considerable.) There have been reports that, contrary to SALT II, the Soviet Union has 'encrypted the telemetry' from some missile tests, i.e. put into code the messages relayed from the missile indicating its operational performance.

3 The United States is moving to fill the gap between Soviet and American counter-force capacity, (a) by developing the MX missile,

yet it is 6 or 7 years away from an initial capability, and its deployment in a comparatively invulnerable mobile system may never occur, because of cost; and (b) by developing long-range GLCMs and SLCMs, yet the deployment of these is prohibited under the SALT II *Protocol* until after December 1981. The opponents of SALT believed that ratification of SALT II would induce an attitude of complacency in America, that the United States would be under great pressure to extend the *Protocol*, and that a president such as Carter would have been likely to accede, just as he cancelled the B1 bomber as a replacement for the B52, stopped for a time the development of the enhanced radiation weapon or neutron bomb, and switched his position over deploying it in Europe. President Reagan and his advisers appear to be of sterner material, but by putting the whole SALT process back to negotiation, he has in effect deferred a decision on both SALT II and the *Protocol*.[13]

If one accepts — as most people do — that in ICBM terms the American force is vulnerable to a Soviet first strike, there is little that the United States can do quickly, irrespective of what happens to SALT II. The opponents of SALT feel that it will prolong, even perpetuate, American inferiority. They would like to see the United States return to a position of continuing strategic nuclear superiority, at whatever cost — by building heavy ICBMs, hardening all existing sites, and perhaps revoking the ABM treaty and investing in missile defence systems. They entirely distrust Soviet assurances. They see the USSR as determined on world conquest and as believing it could 'win' a nuclear war. They point to the more sophisticated Soviet shelter programme[14] as evidence of readiness to conduct nuclear war, and to official Soviet military doctrine which makes nuclear weapons an intrinsic 'warfighting' component of the Soviet armoury.

One cannot entirely discount all these complaints but the remedies appear worse than the disease. Despite a renewed confidence (in some quarters) in ABM technology, to abrogate the ABM treaty would open a Pandora's box of immensely expensive partial defences, and partial defence in this area is little improvement on no defence. The MX, if it is developed and deployed, is a new generation weapon, and should significantly upgrade US ICBM capacity. The USSR seems to have gone beyond the constraints of SALT I, but not extensively nor in a clear-cut way; it may do so for SALT II, but again it is premature to assume this will happen significantly. Over the whole range of the nuclear capacities of the two superpowers, there is still a rough equality. The question is whether superiority in one area may give an advantage usable by constraining the political will of the weaker party, and thus increase the risk of war.

The Soviets took the SALT negotiations seriously, as offering constraints on nuclear escalation and on the risk of nuclear war. They made a number of concession during the negotiations, as did the Americans. The world is in a situation, for the first time, where the Soviet Union does have a perceived, significant strategic nuclear advantage in its first strike capacity against US ICBMs, partial and temporary though it may be. It also has a theatre nuclear advantage in Europe (see next section) because of the deployment of the SS-20s and *Backfire* bombers. It has a clear advantage in conventional forces in Europe and a massive preponderance of tanks. All this would appear to demonstrate that, for whatever reasons, the Soviet objective is not parity but superiority.

Many Americans have come to that conclusion, and their dislike of it and of its implications was compounded first by the Cuban troop crisis of October 1979 and then by the Soviet invasion of Afghanistan in December. The first demonstrated the obstinacy and outreach, the second the lawlessness, the deceit (so Mr Carter said) and the greed for territory and power of the Soviet government. SALT II lost much of its already barely adequate support. Its opponents who had complained that it left the United States dangerously vulnerable were confirmed in their sense of danger. The Agreement, so apparently close to ratification, was put into cold storage from which it can only emerge transformed by subsequent renegotiations. Its timetables are now anachronistic. Yet both superpowers have to look at the implications of losing the constraints to which SALT II agreed, the cost of faster, less manageable nuclear escalation, not only in financial terms but even more in terms of the psychology of confrontation, the rising tide of fear and the impetus to lateral nuclear proliferation.[15]

The strategic nuclear equation and the risk of war

Some strategic analysts seem to assume that a significant imbalance, even in selective systems, increases the risk that they will be used, and yet, since the initial experimental climax to World War II, no nuclear weapons power has used such weapons against anyone. So far as we know, only three times has their use been threatened: when Eisenhower raised the possibility against China in order to bring an end to the Korean War; by the US to deter a Chinese attack on Taiwan in 1958; and by the Soviet Union against China in 1969.

The 1962 Cuban missile crisis is usually considered to have brought the world to its closest proximity to nuclear war, but we do not know how close that was. The American government's understanding of its nuclear weapons superiority at that time, apparently confirmed by the spy Penkovsky, undoubtedly gave it confidence in dealing with the USSR and in forcing the issue, but it was only one factor. The other factors were: (a) the US capacity to deploy overwhelmingly superior naval forces in the vicinity of Cuba, and if necessary land and air forces as well; (b) Cuba's proximity to the United States, and its considerable significance for American security; (c) the psychological relevance of the Monroe Doctrine, and of American righteous indignation at Mr Khrushchev's blatant untruths over the existence of the missiles; and (d) the fact that American reconnaissance discovered the Soviet missiles before they were properly positioned or, in many cases, before they were even in the country.

In these circumstances the United States was able to draw a maritime line and warn the Soviet Union not to allow its missile-carrying ships to cross it except at the risk of local military conflict in which the American forces were unquestionably superior. After some negotiations and adjustments the Soviet Union backed down and took its missiles away. There was no sense in doing anything else, given American apparent capacity and resolve. There appeared to be no other options.

But what if the Soviet navy had been at its present strength, and in position and ready to defend the missile-carrying ships? It is less likely that the United States would have issued its ultimatum. What if the missiles had been positioned in Cuba and ready fo fire before the US found out about them? This again would have been difficult for the US. Conceivably the American airforce could have been ordered to destroy them, in a quick strike, by conventional means, but this would have been an act of war against both countries. What if, instead of Cuba, the missiles were put on Guyana, a former British colony? What if the strategic nuclear balance in 1962 had been closer to parity? One assumes that the Americans would have been much more cautious.

These speculations may not be very profitable, but they do indicate that notions of strategic nuclear superiority or inferiority are only one input into the calculations, and their relevance will depend on an assessment at the time of the circumstances in which either party might be prepared to use nuclear weapons.

There is one highly plausible school of thought which considers that so long as any unacceptable nuclear retaliation is possible, no country will initiate the use of nuclear weapons. Therefore, the risk of war between the superpowers is of a different order. It depends on the importance of the objectives aimed at, the local balance of conventional force, and, above all, on which side is able to 'draw its line' first. In the case of Cuba in 1962, the Soviet Union did not have its line properly drawn (i.e. the missiles installed) before the United States drew its line (at sea, by warships in position). The Soviet Union had to cross this line, at risk, or withdraw — it withdrew. The Soviet Union drew its line around Angola in 1975, with a brief hiatus in the middle while the US Congress debated then rejected Kissinger's advice to counter it. In Cuba in 1979, in the strange case of the Soviet 'combat brigade' which President Carter would have liked to have seen removed, the Soviet Union had its line drawn and the US was unprepared to cross it. A Soviet line is drawn around Afghanistan. President Carter, through the 'Carter doctrine' (see Chapter 5) attempted to draw a line around the Gulf, but it was plainly incomplete. In other scenarios, one could conceive that the Soviet Union might draw a line around an occupied Yugoslavia, or the United States around Saudi Arabia, and so on.

Yet drawing the line is only one of the three factors given above. Further, governments do not ignore the risks of nuclear war: on the contrary they spend immense effort in calculating those risks and their implications for a variety of foreign policies, for one simple reason — uncertainty as to how the other side will act. The American uncertainty must be far greater than the Soviet because so little of the Soviet debate and so much of the American is in public and because so little official Soviet military information and so much American is freely available. Nevertheless the USSR can never be quite sure how the American government and defence machine will act, nor how effectively. That uncertainty must act as a constraint on the Soviet Union.

There are, of course, many constraints against the use of nuclear weapons other than doubt as to whether one would 'win' a nuclear war. Public fear of the consequences is a major constraint; there is a powerful climate of opinion worldwide against initiating nuclear war. A decision to go to war, nuclear or conventional, involves immense costs, 'win' or 'lose'. The use of any kind of nuclear weapon is not a controllable option. No-one knows to what ultimate catastrophe it might ineluctably lead.

One of the calculations of those who fear a Soviet counter-force first strike against the US is that the Soviet government would view as acceptable a US counter-strike that destroyed 20 million or so Soviet citizens. There is no evidence to support such a proposition. While Stalin had no compunction about the annihilation of up to 30 million of his compatriots, effectively 'non-citizens', in purges and labour camps, this is very different thing from the destruction of Soviet people and cities, of the USSR itself, by an alien enemy.

Yet, again, one cannot rationally refuse to admit the possibility of nuclear war. The weapons, with their almost inconceivable capacity to inflict devastation, *exist*, manned and ready. The world at any time is potentially only a few minutes away from the process of launching nuclear strikes ranging from a simple demonstration explosion to a holocaust.

Between the superpowers, which have so much destruction to inflict or suffer, we can fairly assume that the use of nuclear weapons is highly unlikely. A much more pertinent question is whether the possibility of their use in a situation of imbalance might open or close political or conventional military options. This involves an assessment by the country faced with the decision — whether superpower, ally, or other involved party — of the will and character of the superpower's leadership and of its electorate. It involves also the wider context of conflicting interests, especially with the two groups of allies in Europe.

Being separated, if only (at their frozen extremities) by the few kilometres of the Bering Strait, the Soviet and American continents avoid that physical contact which historically has proved so often the catalyst to physical conflict. Their heartlands, their vital industries and centres of population and decision, are several thousand kilometres from each other. But in Europe their forces, their friends, allies, clients are face to face, almost gunbarrel to gunbarrel. In Europe and in the Middle East, rather than in some air-launched Armageddon, lie the more immediate potential causes of superpower confrontation.

4 THE MILITARY EQUATION IN THE EUROPEAN THEATRE

The key fact of the military balance in Europe is that one superpower lives there and the other does not. The Soviet Union is a continental power, with its western border in places less than 800 kilometres from the Federal Republic of Germany. So long as the Warsaw Pact holds, Soviet armed forces may operate effectively in Europe on internal lines of communication which have been developed to enable the rapid supply and reinforcement of Pact formations facing those of NATO. Arms, equipment, supplies and reinforcements from the United States, on the other hand, have to cross the Atlantic, the bulk of them by sea voyages vulnerable (in the event of war) to the extensive Soviet attack submarine fleet located there. There are limits to which the United States can station forces so far from home. For the Soviets, 'home' with all its resources is only an hour or two in flying time or takes a day or two to drive from the 'front line'. This situation affects any discussion of comparative force levels.

A second important fact is the different attitudes to expenditure on defence (see Table 10). As mentioned in Chapter 2, the Soviet Union spends much more on defence than does the United States. If they were prepared to change their budgetary priorities the countries of Western Europe could match Soviet military expenditures, but they are not prepared to do so: it would mean accepting a lower standard of living and so long as the United States, with its highly efficient defence industries, retains its vital interest in the security of Western Europe from Soviet domination, the other NATO powers see no reason for making the necessary sacrifices. They have thus lived since 1945 under the American defence umbrella, their security subsidised by the American taxpayer.

These two factors have compelled NATO to adopt a policy of what is called 'flexible response', with a readiness to use both conventional and nuclear forces depending on the situation. Where conventional forces are overrun on the battlefield, nuclear weapons will almost certainly be employed: first battlefield nuclear artillery, then theatre nuclear forces (short or intermediate-range missiles, and aircraft with nuclear weapons). This policy in turn appears to have induced the Soviet armed forces to institute a doctrine whereby nuclear weapons are similarly part of the initial warfighting operations integrated with conventional arms from the start of conflict. Each side appears to assume that it will be defending itself against an attack from the other, yet such is the balance of forces and the nature of attitudes expressed that for the foreseeable future any conventional attack by NATO on its Eastern neighbours is scarcely conceivable. In recent years, also, there apparently has been a shift in Warsaw Pact doctrine to allow for any war to be fought only by conventional means, at least in the initial period.

The theatre nuclear equation

The physical proximity of the Soviet Union to Western Europe makes it impossible to speak of a theatre nuclear 'balance'. The massive Soviet nuclear forces west of Siberia and the Soviet SLBMs must be presumed to be capable of deployment against Western Europe, even though it is widely considered that Soviet central systems (ICBMs) are not so targeted. Similarly, some of the American strategic nuclear weapons, notably SLBMs, are available for the defence of the European theatre, and more could be committed there if required. Again, while the numbers of artillery pieces (guns) capable of firing nuclear shells is known, the number of shells available is not. Likewise, both Soviet IRBMs and (to a lesser extent) American SRBMs, i.e. the SS-20s and the Pershings, are capable of being reloaded with a second or third missile.[1] The size, range and effectiveness of weapons systems vary. Both the USSR and the US can deploy carrier-borne aircraft for nuclear strikes against each other. Britain and France have air-borne and submarine-borne nuclear weapons, subject to periodical upgrading. The capacity of either side will vary with the degree of warning given. We can only guess at the survivability of weapons, their reliability, their capacity to penetrate defences. Thus one cannot set out a statistical balance of theatre nuclear forces except on the basis of a number of disputable hypotheses. The International Institute for Strategic Studies in London has made as professional an estimate as is publicly available in its publication *The Military Balance*, details of which are shown in Table 8.[2]

Even on the assumptions made, the balance varies according to whether one includes on the Western side Poseidon SLBMs located off Europe and available for use in a theatre of nuclear exchange. If Poseidon missiles are excluded, i.e. if one calculates simply on land-

Table 8 *Long- and Medium-Range Nuclear Systems for the European Theatre*

Category and type	Range/ combat radius	First deployment	Inventory	Warheads per system	Warheads available (approx.)	Arriving warheads (approx.)	Operating countries and notes
							(USSR unless noted)
WARSAW PACT							
IRBM	(nm/km)						
SS-20	2 700/5 000	1977	160	3	285	205	MIRV (? 1 reload per system)
SS-5 *Skean*	2 200/4 100	1961	60	1	40	17	
MRBM							
SS-4 *Sandal*	1 000/1 900	1959	380	1	280	91	
SRBM							
SS-12 *Scaleboard*	490/900	1969	650	1	390	205	
Scud B	160/300	1965					
Scud B	160/300	1965	18	1	14	7	GDR
SLBM							
SS-N-5 *Serb*	600/1 120	1964	60	1	27	13	On 13 G-II, 7 H-II subs
SS-N-4 *Sark*	200/380	1961	9	1	4	2	On 3 G-I subs
Ballistic missile sub-totals			1 337		1 040	540	(52% of available warheads)
Aircraft	(km)						
Tu-22M/-26 *Backfire*	4 025	1974	75	4	96	40	
Tu-16 *Badger*	2 800	1955	318	2	178	47	
Tu-22 *Blinder*	3 100	1962	125	2	70	22	
Su-24(Su-19) *Fencer*	1 600	1974	370	2	118	34	
MiG-23/-27 *Flogger B/D*	720	1971	1 300	1	208	65	
Su-17 *Fitter C/D*	600	1974	640	1	102	29	
Su-7 *Fitter A*	600	1959	165	1	23	4	
MiG-21 *Fishbed J-N*	400	1970	1 000	1	160	38	
Air-delivered weapon sub-totals			3 993		955	279	(29% of available warheads)
Warsaw Pact totals		1971/80	5 330		1 995	819	
NATO							
IRBM	(nm/km)						
SBPS S-3/3	1 600/2 000						

	Range	Year					
Pershing 1A	390/720	1962	180	1	162	91	US, FRG
SLBM							
Polaris A3	2 500/4 600	1967	64	1	28	20	Britain MRV; MARV (*Chevaline*) entering service
MSBS M-20	1 600/3 000	1977	80	1	36	26	France
Ballistic missile sub-totals			342		242	145	(60% of available warheads)
Land-based aircraft	(km)						
Vulcan B-2	2 800	1960	57	2	79	19	Britain including OCU aircraft
F-111E/F	1 900	1967	156	2	125	45	US aircraft in Europe
Mirage IVA	1 600	1964	33	1	23	6	France
Buccaneer	950	1962	60	2	42	10	Britain some aircraft are grounded
F-104	800	1958	318	1	67	6	Belgium, FRG, Greece, Italy, Netherlands, Turkey
F-4	750	1962	40	1	10	2	Turkey
F-4	750	1962	324	1	78	14	US Europe-/dual-based aircraft
Jaguar	720	1974	80	1	32	6	Britain, France
Mirage IIIE	600	1964	30	1	12	2	France
Carrier-based aircraft	(nm/km)						
A-6E	540/1 000	1963	20	2	16	4	US
A-7E	480/900	1966	40	2	32	6	US
Super Etendard	300/560	1980	12	2	10	2	French
Air-delivered weapon sub-totals			1 170		526	122	(23.2% of available weapons)
NATO totals (excluding Poseidon)			1 512		768	267	
US Central SLBM *Poseidon C-3*	2 400/4 500	1971			400	288	
NATO totals (including Poseidon)					1 168	555	

Source: The Military Balance 1980–1981, International Institute for Strategic Studies, London, pp. 118-9. The 21 assumptions on which the statistics are based on given in notes to the original tables, from which these details are extracted.

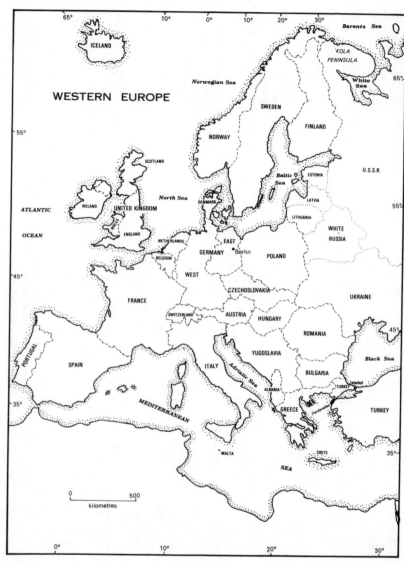

1   Europe

based nuclear weapons in the theatre, the Warsaw Pact advantage
in the number of warheads estimated to arrive at their targets in a
complete exchange is 819 compared with 267 of NATO, i.e. an
advantage of 3:1. If Poseidon is included, the NATO number goes

up to 555, the Pact advantage is 1.5:1. These figures are crude in the extreme, involving a variety of ranges and warheads, and they give only a general indication of the theatre nuclear equation. Even so, that indication suggests a growing theatre advantage for the USSR. This is why there has been so much concern in NATO about 'modernising' their theatre nuclear forces (TNF) with a new generation of longer-range Pershing missile, and with ground-launched cruise missiles. The Soviet conventional force superiority is steadily advancing. More importantly, although NATO aircraft can deliver nuclear weapons into the Soviet Union, no existing NATO theatre-located missiles can reach there, whereas the USSR has a greater and growing capacity to use medium-range missiles against Western Europe and its existing TNF. That capacity is increasing especially because of the deployment within the Soviet Union of the SS-20 mobile missile, with considerable accuracy and a range of up to 3 000 km, and the location of *Backfire* bombers in Eastern Europe. The figures in Table 8 include an inventory of 160 SS-20s as at late 1980, but more are expected at the rate of about 50 launchers per year. *Backfires* are being produced at the rate of at least 30 per year.

Unless provoked by a Soviet first strike, no American government, without the most careful consideration, is going to engage in the use of what are clearly strategic nuclear weapons which may be presumed to invite retaliation on the continental United States. Yet NATO doctrine does not make that judgement. The Soviet Union could not reasonably expect that it could use SS-20s from its own soil against Western Europe and escape retaliation on the basis that while the use of the weapons would be 'tactical' any retaliation would be 'strategic'. Hence the US allocation of strategic nuclear weapons to the defence of Western Europe.

The national nuclear weapons armouries of Britain and France should not be seen simply as part of NATO strength, but as also providing to a degree an independent capacity to wage nuclear warfare. Many, probably most, American analysts do not see it that way, so small are the two armouries compared with that of the United States or the Soviet Union. They cannot conceive of circumstances in which either government would act independently of the United States in nuclear questions. They see the two independent nuclear capacities as evidence of national self-esteem, as an expression of political independence and as a process of buying diplomatic influence especially in the Western alliance. While these judgements may be valid, they are not the whole story. The French nuclear arm (the *force de frappe*) and conventional forces do not come within the NATO planning system, although they are complementary to it.

The British have committed their nuclear weapons to NATO and NATO planning but they have also retained the right to use the weapons independently in an emergency. Is either government likely, in any circumstances, to use its nuclear weapons on its own against the Soviet Union and court the inevitable, annihilating retribution?

The question is usually asked in that form. It is not the only question one could ask, but even in those terms the answer is not an unequivocal negative. Indeed, the present British government, at least publicly, would answer affirmatively and has no alternative to doing so because otherwise their nuclear weapons are worthless and all the expenditure on them a waste of money. Upgrading of the British deterrent under the Chevaline programme is well advanced.[3] Neither the British nor the French independent nuclear capacity was intended as a preliminary to annihilation, but on the contrary as a deterrent to annihilation or to some lesser (but almost equally abhorrent) domination: to be able and ready to 'tear an arm off' the Soviet Union if sufficiently provoked.[4]

What would constitute, unambiguously, such provocation? One situation might be if Soviet ground forces overran the British Army of the Rhine and destroyed it. In Hackett's novel *The Third World War*,[5] he has the Soviet Union destroying Birmingham by an ICBM, whereupon Britain destroys Minsk. But might Britain not retaliate if a much smaller target were destroyed? Something less than a full nuclear exchange must always be considered possible. But also, one could conceive of Soviet political demands upon the United Kingdom, backed by threats of nuclear attack, for which the only deterrence might be the threat of retribution. No government in Moscow could be sure that the United States would cave in to nuclear blackmail: it might be more confident but it could never be wholly confident that a British government would cave in. The destructive effect of one or two British SSBNs launching their weapons would be unacceptable to Moscow.*

---

* Each of the 4 UK SSBNs has 16 Polaris A3 missiles, with 3 200-kiloton warheads, i.e. each submarine has a destructive capacity equivalent to 480 Hiroshimas. The British navy could probably only keep 2 SSBNs at sea continuously, the French 3. The nuclear-armed Vulcan bombers are being phased out, being superseded by the European *Tornadoes* with a shorter range, which would need to be equipped with ALCMs. For Britain and TNF modernisation, see below. Both the British and French governments are determined to retain a nuclear submarine squadron. In 1980 after the British government announced the upgrading of its Polaris missiles, it decided to replace its Poseidon submarines by 4 or 5 US Trident submarines, each with 16 missiles with up to 8 independently targetable warheads. (UK Ministry of Defence, *The Future United Kingdom Strategic Nuclear Deterrent Force*, London, July 1980.)

Is escalation inevitable?

This all raises two related questions on which millions of words have been written: Whether the initial use of battlefield nuclear weapons would inevitably lead to an escalation of the nuclear conflict to the strategic level (SSBNs, ICBMs); and whether the United States would feel compelled to use strategic weapons if theatre nuclear weapons were failing to stop a war in Europe. What is known as 'Gaullism' — the policy adopted by President de Gaulle of building an independent *force de frappe* because he did not trust the US government to use nuclear weapons in the defence of Europe and thus risk retaliation against American cities — has steadily widened its range of adherents on both sides of the Atlantic. As former US Secretary of State Henry Kissinger said in Brussels on the fortieth anniversary of the outbreak of World War II: '...it is absurd to base the strategy of the West on the credibility of the threat of mutual suicide.'[6]

In fact, the strategy of the Western powers for the past 30 years, including the 8 years when Kissinger conducted US foreign policy, has been based on something like this 'absurd' premise, not as a primary reaction but as an ultimate one. For most of that time, the United States had a substantial nuclear superiority, but only for the first few years was it invulnerable to Soviet reprisal. The 'logic of escalation' the 'coupling' of the theatre and strategic nuclear forces, with intercontinental mutual destruction as the last rung of the ladder, was generally considered likely to deter the Soviet Union from taking the first step — attacking Western Europe, the bottom rung. What then has changed? Two things have changed, said Kissinger: the strategic nuclear balance, with Soviet counter-force superiority, and the European theatre nuclear balance. And he suggests that American 'resoluteness in crisis' (under a Democratic administration) would be inadequate to decide for nuclear war in such circumstances.

This statement by Kissinger, which was discussed in the previous chapter and which, on the whole, was not supported, caused consternation in the chancelleries of Western Europe except perhaps in Paris where people said they had always believed it. Kissinger appeared to have two objectives: to encourage the US government to develop a greater counter-force capacity, and to encourage the NATO powers to modernise their TNF. He implied that if TNF as one rung on the ladder of 'graduated response' had become shaky, this made it less credible as a deterrent to the Soviet Union at that level, and the United States was thus being asked to cover by its now less credible strategic armoury a wider gap in the West's capacity to respond to Soviet aggression. The West European powers, on the other hand, see the notion of response not simply as a series of rungs on a ladder, but as a variety of alternatives at different levels, the level and nature of response depending on the level and nature of the attack. This was the substance also of Mr Carter's Presidential Directive 59 (see page 50).

It must be remembered that, apart from the small French and British nuclear armouries, all the theatre nuclear weapons in Western Europe are American weapons operating either under a sole American key or in some cases a joint American-West German or joint American-British key system within the NATO planning and control systems. If Kissinger's argument was about NATO's capacity to inflict unacceptable damage on Warsaw Pact forces, it underplayed that capacity. On what possible grounds, for what possible gain, would the Soviet Union take such enormous risks? But if his argument was about American 'resoluteness in crisis', was he saying that that resoluteness would not be up to taking the initial decision for battlefield nuclear weapons? If so, then the whole NATO strategy falls, and American forces in Europe and their dependants there, fall with it — which would make no sense to an American electorate. In any case, French and some British battlefield nuclear weapons are not under American control. If (as a third possible explanation) Kissinger is saying that the United States is prepared to use theatre nuclear weapons against the USSR but not strategic nuclear weapons, this is a distinction that would be less discernible in Moscow, especially once the next generation of Pershing missiles are deployed, capable of attacking targets in the Soviet Union from Western Europe. And why are there US SSBNs 'committed' to NATO?

Kissinger was not representing the United States government when he made this statement, but he did express the concern of many Americans with the shift in the strategic nuclear balance (discussed in Chapter 3), with the psychological problems which this has raised for the United States, with the determination by most Western European states to have their defence subsidised by the US, and with the growing theatre nuclear and conventional Soviet superiority. At President Carter's urging the West European powers had already agreed to a 3% increase in defence spending in real terms for the five years up to 1982. The US itself also agreed to strive for a similar build-up, and currently the administration is projecting a rise of about 5 per cent in real terms for each of the next five years. It is too early to judge how many of the NATO powers will achieve the 3% goal. If the major ones do, they will roughly match current Soviet defence spending and curtail the growing imbalance in conventional forces, provided the USSR does not increase its effort.

The proposed modernisation of the TNF, for which the United

States would bear most of the financial cost, would help reduce the nuclear imbalance. With curious logic, some European governments told Washington that their agreement to TNF modernisation would depend on the ratification of SALT II. One might have thought that without SALT II and the restraints it put on superpower 'vertical proliferation' (ever-more numerous, more powerful, more accurate intercontinental weapons), TNF modernisation would be essential.

But the European electorates, physically so much closer to the Soviet Union and with so much more experience than the Americans of war on their territories, needed to know that arms control measures were underway. The Soviet Union had agreed to SALT II which for all its limitations offered some reassurance against perpetual proliferation and escalating risks. If, by American action, there was to be no limit to the size of weapons the United States wished to station on European soil, more and more Europeans would want to seek alternative forms of insurance. In the wake of the Soviet invasion of Afghanistan and the US Senate's deferral of a decision on SALT II, some Europeans are more prepared to live with modernisation, at least in the short term.

They did not come easily to a decision. While a 'high level group' in NATO was considering the question of modernisation, a 'special group' was looking at arms control measures which could perhaps be introduced in parallel. On 6 October 1979 the Soviet leader, Mr Brezhnev, sought to prevent modernisation by a stick-and-carrot message delivered in Berlin at the celebration of the thirtieth anniversary of the East German regime. He said that the Soviet Union was prepared to reduce the number of medium-range nuclear weapons in Soviet territory provided no additional such weapons were deployed in Western Europe; that it had decided to reduce the number of Soviet troops in central Europe by 'up to' 20 000 and its tanks there by up to 1 000. He offered improved reporting of military exercises, and he solemnly declared that the Soviet Union would never use nuclear arms against states that renounce the production and acquisition of such arms and do not have them on their territory.

The NATO governments, apparently convinced that the Soviet Union had achieved theatre nuclear superiority through the SS-20s and *Backfire* bombers, saw this as an attempt to prevent the West from returning even to equality. They therefore decided in November and December 1979 to augment their theatre nuclear forces and so 'close a gap in the spectrum of escalation and provide increased options for restrained and controlled responses'.[7] On 12 December the NATO Council agreed that 108 Pershing II ballistic missile launchers would be deployed in Western Europe as from about 1983 (to replace the 1 000 US missiles being withdrawn, especially the shorter-range Pershing Is) plus 464 ground launched cruise missiles (GLCMs). Britain, West Germany and Italy agreed to have the weapons stationed on their soil. Belgium agreed in principle, subject to a delay of six months while arms control agreements are monitored. The Netherlands undertook to decide in 1981 whether the weapons would be located there. None of the other member states was prepared to accommodate them. Despite Soviet statements to the contrary, TNF modernisation is compatible at least with the letter of SALT II and of its *Protocol* — if the SS-20 is excluded from the provisions, so should Pershing II be excluded, and the GLCMs cannot be deployed before December 1981.

TNF modernisation, if implemented, may make Western Europe feel safer in the short term but without an arms control agreement the Soviet Union seems bound to respond with a further escalation. It is yet to be seen whether modernisation and the deferral of SALT II will be used by the Soviets as a basis for stopping negotiations on theatre nuclear weapons systems in what has been called SALT III, on some of the other on-going arms control negotiations such as the proposed Comprehensive Test Ban Treaty (CTBT), Mutual Balanced Force Reductions (MBFR), or 'confidence building measures' under the Helsinki Agreement. It is in fact doubtful whether the US military establishment wishes to see a CTBT at this stage. The discussions that have already taken place on confidence building measures indicated a more healthy, less suspicious superpower relationship for a period. But events in Iran and Afghanistan (and especially American reactions to them) following the disturbing change in the strategic and European nuclear balances have set back the processes of detente — certainly for a year or two and perhaps much longer.

The conventional force equation in Europe

For reasons given earlier (see page 58), it is impossible to speak of a 'balance' of conventional forces in Europe, or indeed to know what quantities of men and arms would be made available from the Soviet Union within a given time. There are additional problems of determining the manning strength of divisions, the state of equipment and level of training. In any case not all national armies are organised into divisions.

The Soviet Union has some 173 divisions, of which 46* (including

---

* In late 1980 Chinese Vice-Chairman Deng Xiaoping told a US editor that there are 54 Soviet divisions in the Far East. (*The Christian Science Monitor*, 24 November 1980.)

6 tank divisions) are deployed on 'the border with China and in Mongolia, and 30 in Central and Eastern Europe. Of the 30, 19 (9 tank) divisions are in East Germany, 2 tank divisions in Poland, 4 (2 tank) divisions in Hungary, and 5 (2 tank) divisions in Czechoslovakia. There are no Soviet divisions in either Bulgaria or Romania. There are some 67 divisions in European Russia, and 24 (1 tank) divisions in the Southern USSR (North Caucasus, Transcaucasus and Turkestan). Czechoslovakia, Poland and East Germany can muster 30 divisions between them (at various levels of readiness) and Hungary, Romania and Bulgaria an additional 27 or more division equivalents. The Warsaw Pact has some 76 combat divisions immediately available for use in any confrontation with NATO. Not all are at full strength (see Table 9).

Against these, NATO has assigned about 64 division equivalents, but many of these are not normally deployed in the NATO area, and many are reserve formations needing time for mobilisation and training before being available for operations.

Since the early 1950s, the Soviet Union and its Warsaw Pact allies have had numerical superiority over NATO in conventional forces in Europe. Until recently, this was held to be counter-balanced by NATO's advantage in theatre nuclear weapons, but (as explained above) this is no longer the case. In conventional military technology also the West long had a comfortable lead, but not any more. The Pact has a massive lead in tank strength, as shown in Table 9(4), and in conventional artillery and rocket launchers. NATO has a wide variety of almost everything, including weapons, with consequent multiplication of supply systems. In tension short of war it cannot use French supply lines. The Warsaw Pact on the other hand has standardised equipment, weapons and aircraft, almost all of which are Soviet-designed. In this as in so many aspects, NATO has shown itself a far more nationalistic and less coherent group than the Warsaw Pact. One can understand why Napoleon said (if he did), 'Give me allies to fight against'.

NATO planning is based on the assumption that in the Central region of Europe they will have to meet 80 Warsaw Pact divisions with some 32 NATO divisions equivalents, only 24 of which are at present deployed in the region (the rest are in Belgium, the Netherlands, Northern Ireland, Britain and the United States). A further 8 divisions might be made available by France. Even so it is a considerable imbalance favouring the Soviet Union. Comparatively, the Northern region is even more vulnerable, especially as Norway and Denmark refuse to have other NATO forces stationed on their soil except in a crisis, although joint exercises are conducted from time to time and military equipment pre-positioned there (see Chapter 5).

Table 9 *The Conventional Force European Theatre Balance*

(1) GROUND FORCES AVAILABLE WITHOUT MOBILISATION (DIVISION EQUIVALENTS)

	Northern and Central Europe			Southern Europe[a]		
	NATO	Warsaw Pact	(of which USSR[b])	NATO	Warsaw Pact	(of which USSR)
Armoured	10	24	13	5⅔	6	2
Mechanised Infantry	13	23	13	37⅔	15	2
Airbone	4			⅔		
Totals	27	47	26	44	21	4

a Comprises Bulgaria, Hungary, Romania, Italy, Greece and Turkey.
b Soviet forces in Eastern Europe.

(2) WARSAW PACT REINFORCING FORMATIONS AVAILABLE (DIVISION EQUIVALENTS)

	Category 1[a]			Category 2[b]			Category 3[c]		
	Armd	Mech	Other	Armd	Mech	Other	Armd	Mech	Other
USSR[d]	1	1	8	5	10	—	19	48	—
Bulgaria	—	—	—	—	2	⅓	⅔	1	—
Czechoslovakia	—	—	—	—	—	⅓	2	2	—
Hungary	—	—	—	—	1	—	—	1	—
Poland	—	—	—	—	3	1	—	3	—
Romania	—	—	—	—	2	⅓	—	2	—
Totals	1	1	8	5	18	2	21⅔	57	—

Grand Total 113⅓

a Up to three-quarters of established strength.
b Up to half.
c Essentially cadres only.
d Based in Western and Central Military Districts.

(3) WESTERN REINFORCING FORMATIONS AVAILABLE (DIVISION EQUIVALENTS)

	Active				*Reserve*			
	Armd	*Mech*	*Marines*	*Other*	*Armd*	*Mech*	*Marines*	*Other*
US	2⅓	4⅓	2⅔	5	3	3	1⅓	8⅓
Belgium	—	—	—	—	—	⅓	—	⅓
Britain	—	—	—	1⅓	—	—	⅔	—
Canada	—	—	—	⅔	—	—	—	—
France	5	—	1	6	—	—	—	—
West Germany	—	—	—	—	—	—	—	2
Netherlands	—	—	—	—	⅓	⅔	—	⅓
Norway	—	—	—	—	—	—	—	3⅔
Totals	7⅓	4⅓	3⅔	13	3⅓	4	2	14⅔
Grand Total 52⅓								

(4) MAIN BATTLE TANK COMPARISON[a]

	Northern and Central Europe			*Southern Europe*		
	NATO	*Warsaw Pact*	*(of which USSR)*	*NATO*	*Warsaw Pact*	*(of which USSR)*
Main battle tanks in operational service	7 000	19 500	12 500	4 000	6 700	2 500

(a) Excludes some thousands of Warsaw Pact tanks in reserve, or in independent units, and about 2 500 NATO tanks in reserve.

(5) TACTICAL AIRCRAFT[a]

	Northern and Central Europe			*Southern Europe*		
	NATO	*Warsaw Pact*	*(of which USSR)*	*NATO*	*Warsaw Pact*	*(of which USSR)*
Fighter/ground-attack	160	1 350	930	625	325	70
Interceptors	386	2 050	1 000	202	1 000	400
Reconnaissance	263	550	300	106	200	125

a Excludes about 400 French fighters, US Navy carrier-borne aircraft and dual-based squadrons, and Soviet medium bombers. (*Source*: *The Military Balance 1980–81*.)

Table 10 *Warsaw Pact and NATO, 1980*

	Population (million)	Armed Forces ('000)	Est. GNP 1979 ($bn)	Est. defence exp. 1980 ($bn)
Warsaw Pact				
Bulgaria	8.9	149.0	34.8	1.14
Czechoslovakia	15.4	195.0	85.4	3.52
German Dem. Rep.	16.8	152.0	75.3	4.79
Hungary	10.7	93.0	41.9	1.08
Poland	35.7	317.5	146.1	4.67
Romania	22.2	184.5	91.2	1.47
Total Eastern Europe	109.7	1091.0	474.7	16.67
Soviet Union	265.5	3658.0*	643.0**	156.0***
Total	375.2	4749.0	1117.7	172.67
NATO				
Belgium	9.9	87.9	111.74	3.74
Britain	56.0	329.3	383.2	24.45

German Fed. Rep.	62.3	495.0	761.0	25.12
Greece	9.5	184.5	32.5 (1978)	1.77
Italy	57.0	365.0	317.0	6.58
Luxemburg	.4	.7	4.69	0.05
Netherlands	14.0	114.9	151.3	5.24
Norway	4.1	37.0	46.0	1.57
Portugal	9.9	59.5	21.8	0.6
Turkey	45.5	567.0	45.3 (1978)	2.6
Total Western Europe	326.6	2768.4	2505.8	93.29
Canada	23.8	78.6	224.4	4.24
United States	221.6	2050.0	2368.8	142.7
Total	572.0	4897.7	5099.0	240.23

* Excludes some 500 000 internal security troops, railroad and construction troops.

** Based on official exchange rate ($1 = 0.657 roubles).

*** CIA estimate.

Source: The Military Balance 1980–81.

Notes: 1. Iceland, a member of NATO with a population of 220 000 has no armed forces, but makes facilities available to US and NATO forces.

2. All financial figures in this Table should be treated with caution.

Geography means that both in the initial and the later stages of any conflict, the Warsaw Pact countries should be able to bring up reinforcements much more rapidly. For NATO this will depend on warning times. For some years, NATO warning time was assumed to be 30 days: 7 days to identify a threat and 23 days to attempt to meet it. These were figures plucked out of the air. More recently it has become clear that they underestimated Warsaw Pact mobilisation capacity. One does not know how much strategic warning (indication of a general international crisis building up) would be received, but in terms of the European theatre NATO now assumes it could have only a few days' warning of an attack. In such circumstances, political authority for military forces to act will be vital but one can expect that Soviet Union will do everything possible to confuse or frustrate such decisions.

It would take Western naval forces at least several months to neutralise the Soviet submarine force, and a high proportion (30%?) of NATO's naval and merchant ships in the North Atlantic would be lost in the meantime. Thus in a comparatively short European land war, NATO naval forces might not contribute significantly to it, although they would probably ensure the passage of reinforcements and essential supplies and would in turn inflict heavy losses on Soviet naval and merchant shipping.

Warsaw Pact conventional superiority, even if backed by Soviet theatre nuclear superiority, is not such as to suggest the threat of imminent attack on the NATO powers, even in the more vulnerable areas. Offensive military action anywhere along the line of Europe's division would almost certainly lead to general war and could lead to nuclear war. This is a considerable deterrent. The defender intrinsically has advantages over the attacker: he is fighting on and for his own terrritory; on internal (protected) lines of communication. He knows the ground; the people are his people. The Western powers are economically much stronger than the Pact powers; indeed the latter depend heavily on Western credits, technology and food. What the Warsaw Pact forces do is keep NATO continuously in a state of apprehension, and the Eastern force superiority and the possibility of attack make it difficult for the West to divert military resources from this area to others where crises may suddenly arise or where the Soviet Union may take targets of opportunity.

Areas of potential military confrontation in Europe and the Middle East will be considered in the next chapter, but at this time it does seem that the greatest threat to the stability and security of Europe, with unknown but undoubted consequences for the whole East-West balance and the peace of the world, lies within the Soviet bloc, in Poland. Change may come there in several ways. Peaceful adjustment through a series of concessions by both government (i.e. the Party) and the free trade union movement (Solidarity) is possible, but would be a fragile process. The Polish government may decide to impose its will on Solidarity by a series of violent repressive measures. Given the temper of the country, increasingly resentful of government inefficiency, party corruption and police brutality, this is unlikely to succeed, and would almost certainly produce massive Soviet military intervention and occupation. It is conceivable that order would then be restored with limited bloodshed, but determined, widespread resistance is entirely possible. There is little practical of a military nature that the West could do to help the people of Poland in those circumstances, although much might be done by other means. The Soviet Union undoubtedly could impose a general fiat, but 1981 is not 1939 or 1944. The Polish army is in far better shape, the Polish nation is aroused. Soviet occupation would be established at great cost. It would leave Poland sullen, uncooperative, and developing yet once again a head of rebellious steam. Soviet relations with the West would be gravely impaired for an indefinite period. Many thousands — probably millions — of East Europeans would have their resentment against Soviet authority kindled or inflamed, and the whole of the Eastern bloc would be put under incalculable internal stress.

The Middle East, the Gulf and Afghanistan

Since the opening of the Suez Canal in 1869, which cut several thousand kilometres off the journey from Europe to Asia, since the discovery of oil fields in Arabia, Iraq and Iran, and since the development of the petroleum-fuelled internal combustion engine as the predominant source of energy for industry and transportation, the Middle East has been 'vital ground' to the industrialised West, an area to be dominated at all costs. Britain, France, Germany and Russia competed for control of territory and concessions there. The United States, coming late and diffidently to overseas imperial acquisition, invested heavily in the oil industry. Land or concessions once obtained demanded physical protection, bases, treaties, protectorates, ports, military advisers, and if necessary (as in the two World Wars), the readiness to engage in armed conflict. The creation of a Jewish 'homeland' after World War I and of the State of Israel after World War II gave an added dimension to an already complex situation, especially when Arab states refused to acknowledge its existence and fought war after war to get rid of it. American sympathy for Israel was much more widely based than the Zionist electorate. By committing the United States to the security of Israel, it ensured its survival but hamstrung American diplomacy. Hundreds of thousands of non-Jewish 'Palestinians', encouraged, induced, or forced to leave their homes within the growing area of Israeli control, created a human and political problem which neither the Arab states nor Israeli governments have been prepared to resolve.

The Soviet Union's interest in the region, discussed further below, has not been to acquire oil, which it has not yet needed, but has been mainly to ensure its own communications, and to be in a position to affect the politics of the region and the favours granted to the West. Its treaties with Egypt, Syria and Iraq have been directed to those ends. The arms it supplied made possible the

Arab-Israeli wars of 1967* and 1973. Soviet arms also made possible Iraq's attack on Iran in late 1980. The USSR does not simply fish in troubled waters: it troubles the waters and then fishes in them. (The Western powers, of course, have been far more imperialistic and financially acquisitive in the past.) A direct East-West clash might have occurred in 1956, when the USSR threatened to intervene on Egypt's side. It did not intervene, but the threat may have encouraged the British and French, already under American and other international pressure, to end their incompetent operations to protect the Canal and topple President Nasser.

What threatens the West's interest in obtaining access to Middle East oil and in maintaining free movement of trade? One threat is the regional governments' recently discovered awareness of the great power they can wield if of one mind. Another is political instability, endemic to the area, showing itself in the Arab-Israeli conflict, the unsolved problem of Palestinian refugees, the existence of the Palestine Liberation Organisation, a 'wild card' in the pack, the recurrent inter-Arab or inter-Muslim or other animosities breaking out within and between states and the ever-present possibility of domestic revolution. A third threat is that of Soviet military intervention, direct (as in Afghanistan) or indirect (through surrogates), or of Soviet pressure on local governments to disadvantage the West, as well as to obtain access to local naval and air facilities, thus intruding a Soviet factor into the regional strategic balance and psychology.

The closure of the Canal after the 1956 and 1967 wars demonstrated that it was not the vital waterway, the 'jugular vein of empire', it had been believed to be. A pipeline parallel to the Canal has provided an alternative to tanker passage. Bulk carriers using the Cape route to Europe reduced unit transport costs. But the Canal is still strategically important — perhaps most of all to the Soviet Union which sends ships between the Black Sea and the Indian Ocean. And the right to overfly countries in the region could be an essential part of military operations to protect oil supplies.

Oil

It is primarily in the region of the (Persian) Gulf that the strategic implications of the power relationships are concerned with oil and the industrialised world's dependence on it (see Tables 11).

---

* This war was formally begun by Israel pre-emptively in the context of Arab military build-ups.

Table 11   *Oil*

1   Western Dependence on OPEC Oil 1978

Country	Overall dependence on imports, %	Of which imports from OPEC, %
USA	42	79
Japan	100	84
Canada	12	74
West Germany	96	58
France	99	84

2   World Oil Production 1979

Region	Oil production mb/d	% of World total
North America	12.0	17.7
Western Europe	2.4	3.6
USSR/Eastern Europe	12.3	18.7
Middle East	21.8	33.4
Africa	6.7	10.1
Southeast Asia	2.1	3.3
Latin America	5.5	8.7
Other	2.9	4.5
Total	65.7	100.0

3   World Oil Consumption 1978

Region	Oil consumption mb/d	% of World total
North America	19.8	30.6
Latin America	4.4	6.8
Western Europe	14.9	23.0
Japan	5.5	8.5
USSR/Eastern Europe	11.0	17.7
Other	8.5	13.4
Total	64.1	100.0

Source: BP Statistical Review of the World Oil Industry, 1979.

Table 11   *Oil (cont)*

4   Gulf Petroleum Producing Facilities

	Reserve	Major Oil Fields		Refineries		Loading Terminals		Pipeline Mileage
	Billion barrels	Onshore/ offshore	Active wells	No.	Capacity 000 b/d	Ports	Single buoy moorings	(Major crude carriers)
Iran	60	9/2	330	5	911	5	2	3 720
Iran	36	4/0	160	7	169	2	0	3 690
Kuwait and neutral zone	88	11/2	1 040	5	712	4	3	740
Oman	6	3/0	160	0	0	1	3	?
Qatar	7	1/2	70	1	10	2	5	120
Saudi Arabia	150	7/7	775	3	586	4	7	2 800
United Arab Emirates	34	3/5	275	1	15	6	8	400
Total	381	38/18	2 810	22	2 403	24	28	11 470

Source: John M. Collins and Clyde R. Mark, 'Petroleum Imports from the Persian Gulf: Use of U.S. Armed Force to Ensure Supplies', Library of Congress Issue Brief No. 1B79046, Washington, 5 May 1979. Information is thus prior to the İran-Iraq War.

5   World 'Published Proved' Oil Reserves at End 1979

Country/Area	Thousand million tonnes	Share of total per cent	Thousand million barrels
USA	4.2	5.0	32.7
Canada	1.1	1.3	8.1
Total North America	5.3	6.3	40.8
Latin America	7.9	8.7	56.5
Total Western Hemisphere	13.2	15.0	97.3
Western Europe	3.2	3.6	23.6
Middle East	49.2	55.7	361.8
Africa	7.6	8.8	57.1
USSR	9.1	10.3	67.0
Eastern Europe	0.4	0.5	3.0
China	2.7	3.1	20.0
Other Eastern Hemisphere	2.6	3.0	19.4
Total Eastern Hemisphere	74.8	85.0	551.9
World	88.0	100.0	649.2

Table 11   *Oil (cont)*

Source: BP Statistical Review of the World Oil Industry 1979.

Notes: 1 Proved crude oil reserves are generally taken to be the volume of oil remaining in the ground which geological and engineering information indicate with reasonable certainty to be recoverable in the future from known reservoirs under existing economic and operating conditions.
2 The recovery factor varies according to local conditions and economic and technological changes.
3 Data exclude shale oil and tar sands.
4 Percentages are based on volume.

6   Estimated Ultimate Conventional World Crude Oil Resources by Region (in billions of barrels)

	Known	*Potential*	*Total*
North America	179.8	100–200	280–380
South America	68.4	54–92	120–160
Western Europe	24.6	25–45	50–70
Soviet Union/Eastern Europe	102.4	63–123	165–225
Africa	75.6	45–94	120–170
Middle East	509.9	350–630	860–1 140
Asia/Oceania	50.8	54–104	105–155
Total	1 011.5	689–1 288	1 700–2 300

Source: Richard Nehring, *Giant Oil Fields and World Oil Resources*, Rand Corporation, Santa Monica, 1978, p. 88.

7   World Tanker Fleet[1] 1979

Flag	*Number*	*'000 DW[2] Tons*	*% of Total*
Liberia	755	102 497	31.3
Japan	184	29 265	8.9
UK	253	26 135	8.0
Norway	169	24 940	7.6
Greece	296	20 528	6.3
France	85	15 144	4.6
USA	306	15 071	4.6
Panama	133	10 562	3.2
Spain	71	9 475	2.9
Italy	97	8 845	2.7
USSR	207	6 157	1.9
Singapore	77	5 752	1.8
Fed. Rep. Germany	34	5 749	1.8
Denmark	44	5 419	1.7
Sweden	22	3 986	1.2

Table 11   *Oil (cont)*

Netherlands Antilles	16	2 633	0.8
Brazil	43	2 608	0.8
Kuwait	13	2 308	0.7
Finland	32	2 245	0.7
South Korea	19	2 164	0.7
Iraq	18	2 100	0.6
Saudi Arabia	21	2 060	0.6
India	30	1 971	0.6
China	48	1 726	0.5
Libya	13	1 479	0.5
Portugal	14	1 460	0.4
Netherlands	25	1 309	0.4
Australia	15	577	0.2
Other	285	13 210	4.0
Total	3 325	327 405	100.0

Source: Jacobs & Co., Ltd, in Australian Institute of Petroleum Ltd, *Oil and Australia 1979.*

Notes: 1. Tankers of 10 000 DW tons and above.
2. Deadweight tonnage is total weight, in long tons, of fuel, water, stores, and cargo that a ship can carry.

New oil resources are discovered from time to time, but overall world consumption has continually increased at a greater rate than discoveries, thus steadily depleting known stocks. At the beginning of 1979, total oil resources deemed economically recoverable (at current prices) were considered by Western intelligence to be 650–700 billion barrels. (But see Table 11(6) on estimated ultimate oil resources.) Present consumption rate is about 20 billion barrels per year suggesting a maximum of about 30 year's supply. Although this is a very rough figure which will be affected by new discoveries, conservation, substitution, etc. and although no statistics vary or fluctuate so widely as oil statistics, the figure indicates the kind of time span we are concerned with — less distance into the future, perhaps, than World War II is into the past. Even if twice this time is allowed to us, it is the near future. We must therefore assume that oil will increase steadily in price and reduce in quantities available, its shortage will force the development of alternative forms of energy, and it wil be the subject of increasing strategic military pressures on the more vulnerable areas of petroleum production.

The economies of most major Western countries are heavily dependent on oil supplied by members of the Organisation of Petroleum Exporting Countries[1] (OPEC) of which the Gulf states provide about 60% (see Table 11(1)). Britain, currently self-sufficient in oil from the North Sea reserves, should remain so for the 1980s but on present estimates will thereafter begin to import oil again, and run out of its own oil by the end of the century or shortly afterwards.

The Soviet bloc states are at present in a much less dependent position than the West. Whereas the United States, Canada, Western Europe and Japan produce 22% of world oil production, they consume 64% of world consumption. The Soviet bloc (mostly the USSR, plus Romania) produces 19% of world production and consumes 18% (see Tables 11(2) and 11(3)).

The Soviet Union is the largest single producer of oil in the world today and a major producer of natural gas. It exports both to Eastern and Western Europe in a web of pipelines. How long can it continue to do so? Estimates vary, but at present oil exports account for a vital 35% of Soviet hard currency earnings. The sources of Soviet oil are moving steadily eastwards, with increased problems of extraction and increased dependence on Western technology. Soviet production nevertheless increased by around 5% p.a. in the 1970s and levelled out in 1978 at the present 11.7 mb/d. Western estimates expect a decline by the mid-1980s or a little earlier. Eastern Europe's proportion of Soviet bloc oil production is small and declining.

How much oil does the Soviet Union have? Nobody knows. A 1979 CIA estimate suggests that on present production and consumption (including exports) rates, the USSR has enough oil only for the rest of this century.[2] Since then major new finds have been reported. Rate of extraction from the oil fields in European Russia is declining. Nearly all the increase has been coming from western Siberia, and is costly to extract and transport. We do not know what will be the pattern for future new oil fields. Whatever the absolute limits of Soviet oil reserves — and it could be as little as 25 or 30

Table 12 *Soviet Oil Statistics (in millions of tons)*

	1970	1975	1980	1985
Production	353	491	620–640	650–670
Imports	4.6	7.5	15.0	30.0
Domestic consumption	261.8	368.1	470.0	570.0
Exports:	95.8	130.4	165–185	110–160
to CMEA	40.5	71.7	88	90.0
other communist	9.9	6.0	7.0	5.0
Non-communist	45.4	52.7	70–90	15.7

Source: Unclassified British FCO paper RE.AS January 1978, quoting Soviet statistics and Western estimates.

years at current production rates — the economics of extraction are going to force the Soviet government to look to alternative sources long before its own oil begins to run out. Ordinary commercial purchasing would almost certainly be a cheaper and more reliable method of acquiring oil than intimidation or invasion, but governments do not always base their calculations on such simple factors. The Soviet tanker capacity is 11th on the world list (see Table 11(7)).

Oil is, of course, only one source of energy — and of export income from energy — for the Soviet Union. It is thought to have about 30% of the world's resources of natural gas, enough at present utilisation rates to last the USSR for nearly a century. (It imported a lot of gas from Iran and Afghanistan, although the former has been seriously affected by the revolution[3]). It has large reserves of coal. Recent British estimates show a slow but steady rate of Soviet substitution of gas and coal for oil, a reduced quantity of oil surpluses for export, and a reduced rate of energy consumption growth due to a lower rate of economic growth.[4] In these circumstances, within five years it could not produce oil as a hard currency earner for its bloc partners and for the West at anything like the present rate.

Table 13   *Estimated Soviet Energy Surplus 1980 and 1985, (million tons oil equivalent)*

	1980	*1985*
Total energy	215	175
Made up of:		
Oil	166	95
Natural gas	47	62
Coal	—	16
Primary electricity	2	2

Assuming these estimates are even approximately correct, it would be surprising if the Soviet Union does not take steps quite soon to supplement its oil resources. The nearest available are in Iran, which, until the war with Iraq, was producing about 2.5 mb/d, although capable of twice that amount. Iran has been estimated to run out of oil by the end of the century, but new finds could change that situation. Iraq normally extracts some 3 mb/d, and is thought to have immense undiscovered reserves. The OPEC state with the greatest production (9.5 mb/d) and largest known reserves (150 billion barrels) is Saudi Arabia.

The Soviets face several dilemmas: 1. they need the latest Western oil-extraction technology, especially for off-shore production, and this requires the goodwill of the governments concerned, especially the United States; 2. they depend on the hard currency obtained from their oil exports in order to import capital goods, technology, and food from the West; 3. they have aroused anger, suspicion and resentment throughout the Muslim world which is the principal source of non-communist oil. The Western powers, on the other hand, face the dilemma that the area on which they depend for the energy to maintain existing industries is many thousands of kilometres away from them; it is politically fragmented and precarious, lacks the protection of Western military bases, and includes two states patently hostile to the United States (Iran and Iraq), one (Saudi Arabia) that is increasingly equivocal in its stance, and another (Kuwait) that is buying sophisticated Soviet weaponry.

Saudi Arabia — the uncertain vital ground

Saudi equivocation appears to be related to anger over the Egypt-Israel settlement, to an emerging contest for power within the Saudi royal oligarchy, the spectre-raising example of Iran, and the uncertain writ of the government as demonstrated by the attack on the Grand Mosque at Mecca in December 1979. At the same time, the Saudi government continues to buy large quantities of American arms and was offended by the Soviet invasion of Afghanistan.

While there are some similarities between Saudi Arabia and pre-revolutionary Iran — both Muslim states, monarchies, dependent on oil exports, having a close military relationship with the US, with large gaps between rich and poor — there are also many points of difference. Saudi Arabia is already a very conservative Islamic state, Sunni rather than Shiah, with much less tradition of religious interference in government. Rule is oligarchical rather than monarchical. Saudi Arabia has a much smaller population, and it is more homogeneous (except for the 1.5 m Yemeni immigrant workers) than is Iran. With a population of about 4 million and an annual oil export income of over $30 billion, Saudi Arabia is in a much better position to satisfy the rising expectations of all social groups than was the Shah. It has no border with the Soviet Union. Even so, it must be assumed that there are radical elements in the country, playing on real grievances, waiting their opportunities. The Saudi government has been ambivalent about North Yemen: there have been unconfirmed reports that it delayed the supply of arms to the North when it was under attack from the South, but North and South are in a curious relationship with each other, and the North has obtained arms from both the US and the USSR. After the

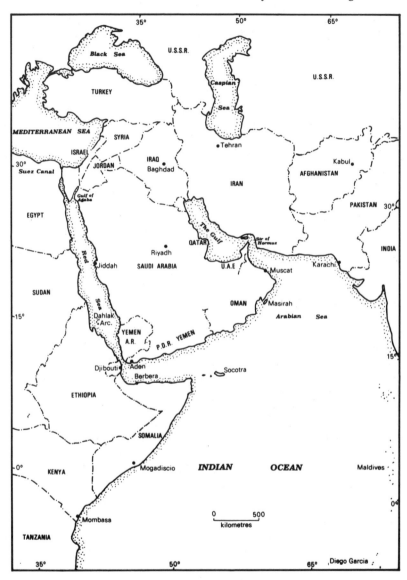

2 The Middle East

Soviet invasion of Afghanistan, visiting American officials sought greater access to Saudi facilities, if necessary, for American forces, and were denied them other than to station AWACS intelligence-gathering aircraft. Such at least was the impression publicly given. Kenya, Somalia and Egypt were more forthcoming.

The 'vital ground' for the control of oil from the Gulf-Saudi peninsula area comprises the oil fields of Saudi Arabia, Oman, Kuwait, Iraq and Iran (strung around the north, west and south-west of the Gulf), the Shatt-al-Arab, the ports of Umm Qasr and Abadan, the Gulf itself but especially the Straits of Hormuz and to a lesser extent, the Suez-Red Sea passage.

Straits of Hormuz

Of these areas, a 'choke-point' at which pressure could be applied is in the Straits of Hormuz, through which about 120 tankers pass each day. At its narrowest, the Straits are 48 km wide, of which the channel, or channels, take up about 3 km. It is thus not possible to sink a few ships and block the passage, as with the Suez Canal, and the only way to prevent transit would be to mine the waters or to insert a naval warship blockade. Mining is an indiscriminate use of force, destructive to friend, foe and neutral alike. Coastal artillery in Oman could probably sink ships in the Straits; it would need Western intelligence in order to distinguish friend from foe. A naval blockade can be selective, but any of these actions could and would be regarded as an act of war. When both the Soviets and the Americans put naval task forces into the Gulf, the Straits of Hormuz was added to the seam of Europe as a place for gladiatorial confrontation, thereby increasing the risk of conflict by miscalculation.

It is true that terrorists from one of the Gulf states or islands could be used to attack the tanker traffic, but only in a limited way. This would be a nuisance, but probably not a *casus belli*.

The Soviet strategic position

The Soviet Union is in a much better position today than ten years ago to bring pressure to bear on this whole area, and the US is in a much worse one. Soviet backing of the Mengistu government in Ethiopia, use of its own developing facilities in the Dahlak archipelago, and its special position in South Yemen with access to former British bases at Aden and the airfield at Socotra, make it the most influential external power on the west of the oil-rich peninsula. Its forces now border Iran on two sides. It supplies arms to Iraq and has access to Umm Qasr, even though Iraq is an uneasy partner, and insensitively keeps executing local communists. From airfields in western Afghanistan the Soviet Union could strike anywhere in the Persian Gulf or the Gulf of Oman. From Soviet Azerbaijan it could strike south to the Iranian oil fields. It has a small surrogate party (Tudeh) in Iran, and has been assiduously building other radical and minority support. It would nevertheless have trouble in mounting naval or ground operations in the Gulf-peninsula region.

The US, on the other hand, has only limited access to bases; it has a precarious use of Bahrein; its own nearest facility is at Diego Garcia in the Indian Ocean. Oman, with British advisers, is essentially pro-Western in its present ruler's orientation, which helps secure the Straits (while the ruler remains) and offers the use of the air base on Masirah Island. The US has negotiated the use of facilities at Oman, but they must be considered vulnerable to both political and military action. It has also obtained access to small naval facilities in Kenya. It can deploy naval air power from its carriers.

The Soviet Union's recent advantages do not mean that it can manipulate the region as it wishes. It can now bring additional pressure to bear, but not without cost to itself. Except for Afghanistan and South Yemen (PDRY), it has none of the regional states 'in its pocket', no access to facilities or political support on the western side of the Gulf, and Afghanistan is prickly and scratchy, an uncertain host, with troublesome indigenes who insist on defending themselves. None of the other states is warm to Soviet intervention or the Soviet system, even where it seeks or accepts Soviet aid. The outside world does not consist of impassive bystanders. The United States can still bring formidable military strength to bear, as its carrier task forces in and near the Gulf have demonstrated, and other states — especially France, West Germany, Britain, and Japan — share its concern about the security of the Gulf and its vital oil flow. What they would do in a crisis would depend on all the circumstances of the time, but they cannot be ignored in Soviet calculations.

If the Soviet Union wished to have a legal basis for intervention in Iran, it would presumably use Articles V and VI of the 1921 Soviet-Iranian treaty,[5] despite the qualifications contained in a note from the Soviet representative, Mr Rotstein, at the time. The treaty, with its qualifications, was reaffirmed in 1927, and became the legal rationalisation for the Soviet occupation of part of Iran in 1941, an occupation which ended in 1946 only after an ultimatum by President Truman to the USSR and a threat to send an American fleet and troops into the Gulf.[6] In March 1959, the Iranian government officially declared the two Articles 'null and void' but the Soviet Union refused to acknowledge this action.[7] In November 1979, the Revolutionary government denounced the two Articles of this treaty and the whole of the 1959 US-Iranian treaty. The Soviet press reported the latter but not the former, and Soviet officials have stated that they do not recognise the abrogation. One can only conclude that the Soviet government has in mind the possibility that it may one day wish to intervene in Iran, and is determined, however speciously, to retain the semblance of a legal basis for doing so.

The Carter doctrine

In his January 1980 State of the Union address to Congress, President Carter warned the Soviet Union against interrupting oil supplies and enunciated what has come to be called the 'Carter doctrine':

> The region now threatened by Soviet troops in Afghanistan is of great strategic importance: it contains more than two-thirds of the world's exportable oil. The Soviet effort to dominate Afghanistan has brought Soviet military forces to within 300 miles of the Indian Ocean and close to the Straits of Hormuz — a waterway through which much of the free world's oil must flow. The Soviet Union is attempting to consolidate a strategic position that poses a grave threat to the free movement of Middle East oil. . . . Let our position be absolutely clear. Any attempt by any outside force to gain control of the Persian Gulf region will be regarded as an assault on the vital interests of the United States. And such an assault will be repelled by use of any means necessary, including military force.[8]

The 1973 Arab-Israel war showed the United States that even its NATO allies 'ran scared' and were unreliable at that time in the face of Arab pressures. If the United States, provoked by an earlier Soviet intervention or by interdiction of its Gulf oil supplies, wishes to intervene in Iran or the peninsula, it must do so primarily from its maritime forces, although since the rapprochement between Egypt and the US, the latter has engaged in joint exercises with the Egyptians and has access to Egyptian bases. This helped make possible the hostage rescue attempt in Tehran in 1980 and could be a vital facility in more critical circumstances. Yet as recent American studies have indicated[9] the United States would have considerable difficulty in intervening in strength, in the face of local opposition, in any major Middle Eastern state, and could not ensure the continued supply of oil to the West from this region. It could, with difficulty, mine the Straits of Hormuz; this would carry the risk of war, and the complete stoppage of oil supplies. Being so much closer, the Soviet Union is much more capable of airborne intervention. Yet oil fields, pipelines, refineries and port facilities are highly vulnerable installations and a Soviet government could not be more sure than the US of maintaining production and supplies short of a massive military occupation.

One cannot rule out such a possibility in the future. For the present, the Soviet government is adequately engaged in Afghanistan (see below). On all counts, it would seem logical that the USSR will take no overtly offensive action in the near future, will engage in demonstrations to show it is the region's protector from American imperialism, will seek to increase subversive activities in Iran, to subvert or seduce Saudi Arabia away from its Western affiliations, and will come to better terms with Iraq yet not in ways to antagonise Iran. A Soviet military attack on any of these at this stage would set alarm bells ringing all over the world. Much better and cheaper to advance quietly the processes which might bring about a Soviet orientation, or even — in a breakdown of security which it covertly encouraged — an invitation to Soviet forces to assist in the restoration of order. If Afghanistan is a model, the Tudeh party in Iran will try to become a respectable part of government before launching the coup or coups to bring it to sole power.

Israel

Since 1973, when the OPEC states combined to enforce their near-monopoly simultaneously with the Egypt-Syria assault on Israel, the two situations have been inextricably interlinked, with the links reinforced when post-revolutionary Iran refused to be the odd state out by supplying Israel with oil, as the Shah had done. The Arab-Israeli dispute has long been an arena for superpower conflict through proxies, but it was the proxies who had the quarrel and who fought four successive wars under rival superpower patronage. Neither superpower has been able to dominate the region. Neither has been more than an arms supplier, making the wars possible in the first place and preventing decisive victory for the other side at the end. Each has been ejected ignominiously from positions of strength; each is treated with suspicion; and for a decade or more each has roughly balanced and has restrained the other, including at sea in the eastern Mediterranean.

All four anti-Israeli wars have essentially been wars between Egypt and Israel. The triumph of President Carter's Camp David diplomacy with President Sadat and Prime Minister Begin in 1978 was that it removed the likelihood of such a war in the foreseeable future. Egypt has regained at the conference table the territory, the resources, and the security it could not obtain on the battlefield; but it has done so at the cost of the enmity of most of her former Arab partners, all of whom want a solution to the problem of Palestinian refugees and some of whom want the extinction of the state of

Israel. The weakness of Camp David was that it made no inroad on the Palestinian problem and provided no constraint on Israeli expansion into the West Bank region — an expansion on a smaller scale but to Muslim eyes evidently more colonial in nature than the Soviet Union's in Afghanistan. Unchecked Israeli expansion aroused the anger of the other Middle Eastern states against Egypt and the US, strengthened their opposition to Israel and weakened American prestige and influence even though not simultaneously offering equivalent advantages to the Soviet Union. If in existing circumstances there cannot be a major war in the Middle East, nor can there be the promise of peace.

Iraq versus Iran

Not long before the 1973 Arab-Israel war and the oil embargo and price rise, it was conventional wisdom in many places that the Arab states were incapable of sinking their differences in a common cause, or of managing the distribution and marketing of the region's oil. This was shown to be incorrect, at least for a time. When Iraq launched an invasion of Iran in September 1980, the differences surfaced with a vengeance in a process of mutual destruction and economic loss that seemed almost incomprehensible. It divided the OPEC countries and came close to causing war also between Syria and Jordan.

Animosity between peoples of what are now Iran and Iraq goes back for millennia. In more recent times, there have been several sources of tension.[10] In simple terms, the first is control of the Shatt-al-Arab waterway, the common estuary of the Tigris and the Euphrates, which both states use for the export of their oil. By a 1937 treaty, when Britain had a de facto protectorate over Iraq, the waterway became part of Iraq. In 1969 Iran under the Shah abrogated the treaty, using naval escorts to protect its shipping. A second source of tension has been the Shah's support of Kurdish rebels against the Baghdad government. In 1975, by an agreement signed in Algiers, Iraq agreed to the legal division of the Shatt in return for Iran's withdrawal of support for the Kurds, thereby enabling Iraq to put down the rebellion. But the forced division of the waterway continued to rankle with Baghdad. A third source of tension was the Shah's pretension to dominate the Gulf, even expropriating islands in the Straits, a claim not pursued by his successors. A fourth source was the main determining cause of the present conflict: repeated calls by Iranian religious leaders during 1979–80 for the Shiah Muslims of Iraq, who constitute just over half of the population, to rise up in revolt against their Sunni leaders. Iraq presumably hoped to capitalise on Iran's disordered administration, the emasculation of the armed forces by the revolutionary regime, and the sizable Sunni Arab population of the Iranian province of Khuzestan. In the event, the war proved much more difficult and costly to wage. The immediate effect was to stop oil exports by both countries, although both were able to resume some exports — Iraq by pipelines, Iran through Kharg and Lavan Islands. Saudi Arabia and some other states made up most of the shortfall. The Soviet Union continued to supply Iraq with arms, though apparently in reduced quantity, and also, more covertly, sent arms to Iran, hitherto dependent on Western weapons for which spares and replacements had been cut off when Iran took the US Embassy hostages in November 1979. But neither the Soviet Union nor the United States has wished to intervene in this inter-Muslim war, nor did they feel able to capitalise upon it, although both supplied the arms which made it possible and bloody.

One may ask why the United States and the Soviet Union should not leave the oil producing states to get on with the business of producing oil and selling it to them at world market prices. If the commodity were potatoes instead of oil, this would undoubtedly be the best policy. But oil is a vital, coveted, limited and depleting commodity for which, in the near future, the West has greater need but which it is in a weaker position to command. Oil is no pawn in the superpower chess game; it is at least a queen. Probably well within a century it will disappear as an energy-producing resource. It will cause a lot of anguish before it does.

Afghanistan

The Soviet invasion of Afghanistan in late 1979 was but the latest and most definitive stage in a more than 20-year process of escalating Soviet intervention in the affairs of that country — a culmination which demonstrated that the process had failed (as it has so far still failed) to produce a regime able to run the country effectively along Marxist-Leninist lines, however pro-Soviet it might be in its external policies.

Despite the known fierce independence and individualism of the Afghan people — an individualism geared less to national than to ethnic and tribal loyalties — and despite the evidence that the Soviet government was prepared to back several horses simultaneously, it would unduly stretch credibility to assert (as is widely done) that the Soviet Union had no part in the development of a communist movement and in the formation, in January 1965, of the People's Democratic Party (PDP) of Afghanistan, whose organisation and constitution were modelled on those of the Communist Party of the Soviet Union, and those funds were provided from Moscow. Or that the Soviets, with advisers in key places within the government and the communications system, had no part in or knowledge of the coup against the monarchy in 1973, or of the PDP armed forces coup against President Daoud in April 1978*. The two factions into which the PDP had uneasily divided — the *Parcham* ('Flag') group led by Babrak Karmal and the *Khalq* ('Masses') group led by Nur Muhammad Taraki and Hafizullah Amin — must have been confusing or frustrating to their Soviet mentors, who nevertheless found themselves able to support both.

At the time of the 1978 coup, there were reported to be some 350 Soviets in the country, including military advisers. With $400 million of military and economic assistance, Afghanistan was the largest per capita recipient of Soviet aid in that year. Immediately after the coup, the Soviet government set up a communications facility in Afghanistan. The expulsion and denunciation of Babrak and other Parchamis by the Taraki government in July 1978 did not affect the Soviet position. In October the Afghan government introduced a new flag and emblem similar to those of Soviet republics. By early 1979, the number of Soviet military advisers had risen to about 1 000; by June (after an uprising at Herat) to at least 2 500; by early December, after a long visit by General Pavlovsky,[11] Commander in Chief of Soviet ground forces, to about 3 500, operating down to platoon level within the Afghan army. By this time there were also some 2 000 civilian Soviet advisers in Afghanistan in senior managerial and planning positions in the various economic ministries and in the educational system. There was thus no significant part of the armed forces — in their operations, logistics or administration — or of the civil bureaucracy, which was not permeated with Soviet 'advice'. Yet even under this wealth of talent, the nation's administration steadily deteriorated, insurgency was widespread, the armed forces and the clergy disaffected, and several hundred thousand people fled across the border into Pakistan. Amin's assassination of Taraki (whom the Soviet government had publicly supported) in September did not improve matters. The USSR saw Afghanistan sliding out of control — out of their own control and out of the control of a wilful surrogate. After a military build-up at Bagram air base, they intervened on 25–26 December 1979 with massive forces.

---

* It is sometimes said, more credibly, that the pro-Soviet military in 1978, being impulsive by inclination, acted earlier than the Soviet government would have liked.

They murdered Amin (or had him murdered) and introduced the third alternative leader (Babrak) who had been in exile in Czechoslovakia and who allegedly retrospectively requested the Soviet invasion under Article 4 of the Treaty of Friendship and Co-operation of December 1978.[12] The only threat to the independence and territorial integrity of Afghanistan at this time was patently from the Soviet Union. The threats to internal security were from disaffected Afghans, and still more, in Babrak's words from abroad on 27 December, by the late ruler who had caused them to be disaffected. Babrak referred to:

> imprisonment, enforced migrations, barbarous and inhuman tortures and martyrdom and killings of tens of thousands of our mothers and fathers, brothers and sisters, sons and daughters which took place under Hafizullah Amin and on the direct orders of this bloodthirsty butcher.[13]

Soviet explanations of their invasion were thus transparently incorrect: that they were invited by the Afghan government, and that this was to counter interventions by the United States, China and Pakistan. This very transparency demonstrates that, when taking an opportunity to expand its area of control, the Soviet government is not troubled by the lack of a legal basis or of an internationally acceptable rationale. It is understandable that Yugoslavia condemned the invasion; it is somewhat more surprising that Romania had the courage to indicate its disagreement.

Various explanations can be put forward for the Soviet action. The Soviet Union, it is said, could not afford to see a neighbouring Marxist state slide into anarchy, as this would discredit the communist cause. It could not afford to see a neighbouring Muslim state up in arms against its communist rulers, as this would evoke sympathy and even perhaps emulation from the 45 million Soviet Muslims many of whom (including Uzbeks and Tadzhiks) live in the southern region of the Soviet Union. It could not permit another Iran on its border. The United States would probably accept the intervention as not wholly unreasonable, the argument goes, as Afghanistan had already passed into the Soviet sphere of influence. In any case the USSR could afford to anger the United States, which had provoked the Soviets by pressing for TNF modernisation in Europe, which had been thrown out of Iran and was now preoccupied by the Tehran Embassy hostages. The US Senate was unlikely to vote for ratifying SALT II in the near future, so that would not be affected. There was a weak, probably one-term president, without the will or the capacity to do anything about the Soviet invasion. The USSR probably assumed that most other states would accept the Soviet occupation as a *fait accompli* sooner or later. We have no way of knowing for certain whether or how far these assessments

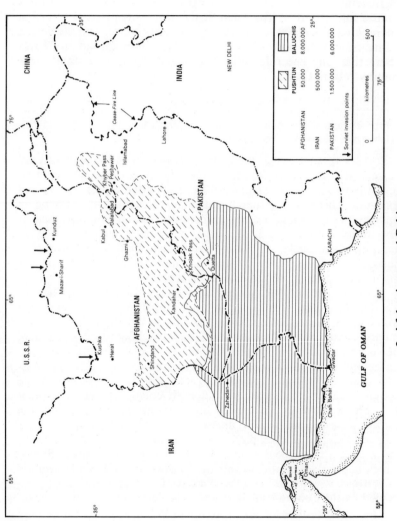

3 Afghanistan and Pakistan

are correct. If they are correct, they involved a degree of miscalculation at least in the short term, as American and non-communist world reactions have shown, especially from Muslim states, and from Yugoslavia.

Unfortunately the 'sphere of influence' argument has touched a sympathetic chord in the West, especially in continental Europe where governments have lived with the concept for centuries, where Afghanistan is almost unknown and certainly uncared for, and where the daily preoccupation is how to live alongside the Soviet military, political and economic machine. West European protests against the Soviet invasion have no doubt been genuine enough but there has been little sense that anything practical could or should be done about it. What can't be mended is best attended. This attitude ignores the potential precedent set by Afghanistan; the fact that ten years ago it was a neutral state, not in the Soviet sphere of influence, not permeated by Soviet advisers, not occupied by Soviet troops. The enormity of the Soviet action lies in the contempt it showed for the independence of a Third World neighbour and for Western opinion. What may now appear to give the USSR some sort of 'right' and reason for further intervention is the end product of a process of escalating interference, an interference which quite patently has helped to generate the internal circumstances on which invasion was 'justified'. The Soviet government may well find that it has bitten off a very indigestible people in Afghanistan, but the opposition so far is badly armed and co-ordinated, and is difficult to supply. Resistance will continue; it will be irritating, but what will it be able to achieve?

Those Western governments that have reacted most strongly to the Soviet invasion — the United States and Britain — have expressed their concern primarily in terms of the strategic implications and presumed motives of the Soviet government: 1 that this is one further step in the traditional Soviet desire for 'warm water' ports on the Indian Ocean; and 2 that the occupation of Afghanistan will enable it to bring greater pressure on the Gulf oil-producing states and thus influence the flow and cost of the oil on which Western economies depend.

Soviet Indian Ocean ambitions

How traditional, how contemporary, is Soviet desire for its own access to the Indian Ocean? Peter the Great (Tsar 1682–1725), who by territorial conquest won for Russia access to the Baltic, the Black and Caspian seas,[14] would have expanded further south if he could. In fact his forces temporarily occupied Iran's northern province of Gilan. In his Will, published only in 1775, Peter said that whoever succeeded him should move southwards to Constantinople and India, for 'whoever governs there will be true sovereign of the world'. In a series of wars with Iran between 1796 and 1828, Russia acquired further Iranian provinces which are now part of the Soviet Republics of Azerbaijan and Armenia. A great deal of British defence and diplomatic activity in the nineteenth and early twentieth centuries was devoted to containing Russian pressures in the direction of the Indian sub-continent. Although one should perhaps not give too much weight to it, in a secret protocol to the pact arranged in 1940 (but never signed) between the Soviet Union, Germany, Italy and Japan, the Soviet government declared that 'its territorial aspirations centre south of the national territory of the Soviet Union in the direction of the Indian Ocean'.[15] On 26 November 1940 a memorandum from Schulenberg, German Ambassador to the Soviet Union to his Foreign Office in Berlin reported that the Soviet government accepted the draft treaty 'provided that the area south of Batum and Baku in the general direction of the Persian Gulf is recognised as the centre of the aspirations of the Soviet Union.'

What may be possible under the aegis of a general war may well be impossible in a time of general peace, but at least the two quotations show the content of Soviet ambitions at that time. During the war, the Soviet Union and Britain jointly occupied Iran, and the former removed its troops ofter the war only belatedly and under strong international pressure. It unsuccessfully laid claims to the Turkish provinces of Kars and Ardahan. The term 'warm water port' is highly evocative, but do the Soviets need such an outlet on the Indian Ocean? Would they benefit significantly from it?

Access to other people's facilities must always be considered precarious, as the Soviet expulsion from Berbera demonstrated, and such access is less satisfactory than having one's own. There is no vital Soviet strategic or economic interest that requires the Soviet Union to have its own port on the Indian Ocean. Such a facility if appropriately placed on the end of a Soviet railway line might serve the growing Soviet trading and maritime interests in that region, including the naval presence permanent since 1968, and it might put the Soviet government in a much better position to further exploit political or strategic opportunities that may occur. The southern border of Afghanistan is less than 500 kilometres from the Gulf of Oman. But the economic costs of a railway through this terrain would be enormous; it would be vulnerable to land interdiction and to local political pressures. It is a great deal easier to draw on a map than to put on the ground.

Three countries separate the Soviet Union and Soviet-occupied Afghanistan from the Indian Ocean: India, Pakistan, and Iran. It would make no sense on any grounds for the Soviet Union to alienate or threaten India, its most 'natural' ally against China, and a country with nearly 700 million people and almost as many problems. The USSR has no common border with Pakistan, but Afghanistan does — the Durand line which was negotiated by the British in the nineteenth century. It arbitrarily but porously divided two strongly cohesive regional or tribal groups: the Pushtuns (or Pathans) and the Baluchis (see map on page 94). Each group has long been a source of disaffection against the Pakistan government, attenuating its control and thus weakening the nation.

Regional and religious aspects

At the time of the independence of Pakistan (1947), Afghanistan raised the possibility of an autonomous Pushtunistan (or Pakhtunistan), and denounced the Durand line. There have been periodic armed border incidents over the years. Pushtuns comprise half the Afghan population (and 13% of Pakistan's). Taraki and Amin were and Babrak is a Pushtun, but much of the armed resistance to the Kabul governments since April 1978 has been from Pushtuns, and accordingly most of the refugees in Pakistan are the same. Although Pakistan's President Zia ul-Huq has sought to dissociate himself from the refugees, some of whom are undoubtedly using Pakistan as a safe haven from which to launch insurgency in Afghanistan, he cannot dissociate Pakistan from those activities, and he understandably fears Soviet or Soviet-backed Afghan attacks. Babrak, who can hardly expect the Pakistani Pushtuns to support him, nevertheless added to Pakistani apprehensions by restating (on 10 January 1980) the continuing Afghan view that 'no border exists between Afghanistan and Pakistan and this issue has not been settled'. The existence of the Pushtuns will continue to provide a basis for fomenting discord between the two states.

Although the Pakistani Pushtuns have shown a strong degree of regional independence, they have done so on the whole within the framework of the Pakistani state system. Not so the Baluchis, a nomadic people with hereditary chiefs to whom loyalty is more strongly given than to the central government. Pakistan's 1.5 million Baluchis have never been reconciled to being absorbed into the Pakistani state. They objected to political and economic domination. They rebelled in 1948 and were subdued by military force. They rebelled again in 1973 and for four years engaged some 70 000 Pakistani troops. According to reports, there are still 30 000 troops in Pakistani Baluchistan. Iranian Baluchistan comprises a Sunni Muslim minority in a largely Shiite (Shiah) country — a minority that at different times has received help from Pakistani Baluchis, from Iraq, and has made common cause with Iran's Kurds.

There are varying reports of active Soviet support of the Baluchis in both countries. Baluchi leaders seem to want to keep their distance from the superpowers but the temptation for the Soviet and (on its behalf) Afghan governments to support another major regional insurgency will be great, provided they can gain clear control of Afghanistan itself. Supporting insurgency would be more likely than a confrontation of arms with a Pakistan probably backed by both China and the United States.[16] Some Indians might welcome the ultimate prospect of the complete and final disintegration of Pakistan. Strategically India is far better served by having a buffer state separating it from the USSR. Pakistan is very shaky economically and politically, and the government has a narrow power base. A lot can happen in a few years or months. Who, at the beginning of the 1970s, would have forecast the dismemberment of Pakistan as it then was, or the burning of the American embassy in Islamabad, or a Soviet military occupation of Afghanistan?

The opposition in Afghanistan to the Soviet invasion is normal resistance to alien rule. Pakistan opposed the invasion for what it is: flagrant aggression with practical and symbolic implications for Pakistan's own security. In both Afghanistan and Pakistan opposition to the Soviet action is also based on Islamic considerations. To the extent that in Afghanistan this is a religious rather than a nationalistic factor (and it is not always easy to separate the two), it would seem to stem from: 1 the disruption of village life and the customary authority of village leaders by an insensitive reformist communist government; 2 the antagonism of a religion based on one God (Allah) to a political ideology that denies the existence of God and suppresses religious freedom; 3 the resentment of church authorities against the reduction of their power, the expropriation of their lands, and breaches of their traditions.

Opposition to the communist PDP in Afghanistan and the Soviet advisers and armed forces there resulted in a surprising unanimity among other Muslim governments in denouncing the Soviet invasion. While this may not loosen the Soviet grip on Afghanistan, it will render more difficult both the occupation of the country and the process of seeking further advantages in or against other Muslim states, including Iran.

An 'Arc of Crisis'?

It is too simple to speak, as some do, of the area from Ethiopia to Afghanistan as an 'arc of crisis' or of instability. The word 'arc' is an irrelevant and inaccurate piece of journalist's coinage. Each part of the region has its individual character and problems, yet the whole area is given strategic coherence by the oil wealth of the peninsula plus Iran and Iraq, by the prevalence of Islam in different forms, and by Soviet-Western competition for influence. Over recent years, the Western position along the Soviet Union's southern boundaries has deteriorated and its capacity to compete has been weakened. That competition is what makes the region a tinder box.

The invasion of Afghanistan is the latest move in the Soviet-American power game, and it sets both precedents and a more forward base for subsequent Soviet moves. Some people fear that Iran may be the next candidate victim, which is why Western and world reactions to Afghanistan are so important. The worst feature of that game, which Afghanistan epitomises, is that from Angola onwards the Soviet Union has assumed the failure of American will and capacity to defend the recipients or victims of Soviet influence or power. On this occasion, while anger and brave words were forthcoming from Washington, the capacity to act without seriously depleting the commitments to Europe, was lacking. The spasm of American anger, initiated by the Tehran Embassy hostages and reinforced by Afghanistan, radically affected the American mood and changed majority views on and attitudes to detente. It did not change the mind of President Carter, and he was subsequently rejected by the electorate. In these views, the Soviet Union has returned not to the Cold War but to the pre-Cold War policies of expansion wherever opportunities offer.

The effect of this on American policies has been to strengthen those who see armed confrontation as a strategy, rather than armed strength as the adjunct of a basically political strategy.

But there are positive features. One suspects that Afghanistan will be a difficult country to subdue. The invasion was a reminder to the nations that the world is an unpleasant place to live in, and that neither powerful rhetoric nor naïve trust in the Soviet government is a substitute for military strength. It was a reminder to the USSR of the strength of the Muslim world and of Islam's basic opposition to communism. It engendered new evidence that the United States is again prepared to fight for vital interests outside Europe and the North Atlantic. It was a reminder to the Arab states of the predatory nature of the Soviet regime. It should be a reminder also to the United States that Camp David, for all its merits, was not enough; that the stability of, and lack of hostility from, the Arab world require at least a resolution of the Palestinian problem and that the unrestrained thirst for Middle East oil, half a world away from Washington, confers on America's world position and on world peace alike a dangerous vulnerability.

The world has witnessed in recent years a largely unco-ordinated but undoubted resurgence of Islamic religious fervour, much of it directed against Western institutions and values and given political shape and content through the recent achievement of independence from Western imperial rule. The fact that a group of Islamic states are sitting on a substantial proportion of the world's oil has given them additional power and an incentive to joint international action against the Western states who for so long exploited the oil and still largely depend on it, and who underwrite the security of Israel. Muslims dissatisfied with the maldistribution of wealth, conspicuous consumption and widespread corruption they associated with modernisation and foreign economic and military dominance, have turned in two principal directions: to religious fundamentalism with its high sense of order, and to left-wing radicalism with its preoccupation with 'justice'. To the fundamentalist, there is not a lot to choose between the corrupting materialistic values of the Christian West and the godless materialistic values of the communist Soviet Union.

Iran

All these elements, somewhat simplistically stated, plus a repressive regime, some desire for Western liberal values, the finance of bazaar merchants and a large urban unemployed, combined to bring down the Pahlavi government in Iran. Authoritarian regimes are almost invariably replaced by authoritarian regimes. The Shah, with long experience in government, was replaced by the Ayatollah Khomeini with none. Initially, enough of the bureaucracy remained, and enough of the educated middle class joined or accepted the new administration, to prevent or at least delay a complete dissolution into national chaos; but chaotic elements, whose affiliations are not all identified, as well as Arab guerillas in Khuzestan, keep erupting. Parallel to the armed forces, there is the highly political Revolutionary Guard, responsible not to the government but to the religious authorities. Resentful minorities (especially Kurds, Turkmen and Azeris in the north and Baluchis in the south) add to the uncertainties. The Iranian economy teeters on the brink of disaster, even more precariously since Iraq launched its invasion, although the situation improved after the US released frozen Iranian assets in return for the American hostages held to ransom for 444 days. National disintegration is an ever-present possibility. The internal balance of forces is yet to be declared and resolved as the current successive 'circuses' give way to the need for 'bread' — food and employment. It is with that balance, whatever it may turn out to be, that the two superpowers will have to deal, as best they can. The United States has little leverage, and the Soviet Union has not been able to transmute anti-US feeling into significant political or economic influence.

It would seem unlikely that the country will settle down on the basis of the present disparate pattern of authority, much of it dependent on the aging Ayatollah Khomeini. Iran has a long history of turbulence, and none of democracy. It seems probable that there will be at least one more convolution in the near future and that quite soon. There are several possibilities, e.g. an army takeover, preserving much of the present Islamic orientation but providing for more concentrated and disciplined rule. Or, the disintegration of Iran into its provinces. A revolution from the left fostered by the Tudeh party in association with various radical groups and possibly assisted by the Soviet Union cannot be ruled out. It would be a bloody affair, and could induce external intervention. No-one can say how it would conclude.

The Eastern Mediterranean

The Eastern Mediterranean is an area of potential danger for the East-West strategic balance for several reasons:

1 The United States is committed to the preservation of the State of Israel, and the Soviet Union is prepared to assist those Arab states which would like to see Israel destroyed or at least reduced. This has been briefly considered in the previous section. The eastern Mediterranean coastline also provides the terminals for several major oil pipelines.

2 Soviet merchant and naval shipping based on or serving the Black Sea region can reach open waters only by sailing through Turkish straits — the Bosphorus and the Dardanelles.

3 The two NATO members on the south-western borders of the Warsaw Pact — Turkey and Greece — are in serious dispute in ways which weaken their participation in NATO and thus weaken the Treaty itself as well as their individual resistance to Soviet pressures. Both countries, but especially Turkey, have fragile democratic systems and chronic domestic problems which add to their strategic weaknesses.

4 The Mediterranean fleets of NATO and the Soviet Union, of roughly comparable strength, shadow each other's activities. They act as a restraint on military initiatives and provide opportunities for incidents by miscalculation.

One could say that any Soviet ambitions for control of the Straits constitute a positive danger to peace, and the Greece-Turkey disputes constitute a negative danger.

It would be logical for the Soviet Union to want to control the Straits, jointly if necessary or independently if possible. Central and Southern European Russia has no direct outlet to the open sea; this is a considerable strategic disadvantage. Its main shipbuilding yards are located in what are almost inland lakes — the Baltic and the Black seas. Its main fleet is compelled to operate out of the Kola peninsula in the north.

Thirteen wars have been fought between the Russian and Ottoman empires. The Soviet Union has periodically sought greater control over the Straits, which Turkey has vigorously resisted.[17] The 1936 Montreux Convention[18] defines the rights of passage through the Straits, and Black Sea powers are permitted to send through capital ships (defined as surface vessels of war) other than carriers of more than 15 000 tons. In recent years the Soviet government has flouted the convention by sending two aircraft carriers, *Kiev* and *Minsk*, of 40 000 tons, through the Straits, declaring them to be 'anti-submarine cruisers'. Although there were reports that Turkey protested strongly in private, neither it nor any other party to the convention did so in public, and the effect must be to make the convention not much more than a formality.*

One can be sure that in the event of war, or even in the event of situations short of war, the Soviet armed forces will do everything possible to ensure unimpeded Soviet use of the Straits.

Turkey has both strengths and weaknesses in dealing with Soviet pressures. The economy is in very poor condition; it is badly managed and unlikely to improve greatly, with a massive deficit to other Western powers. Although the democratic processes are under constant strain and currently are suspended, they show surprising tenacity. The army is under constant temptation to intervene but so far it has seen its role as the guardian and referee of the democratic system rather than a more effective permanent alternative to it. Civil violence is endemic. The Turks are a proud, tough,[19] independent people, a former imperial power never itself colonial, reluctant to be imposed upon by ally or enemy. Turkey has the largest army in European NATO. Although Islam is the dominant religion, reli-

---

* If the convention still has teeth, against whom might they be used? Would Turkey risk tension or even conflict with the USSR by refusing the passage of large Soviet warships? Might not a Turkey under pressure from the USSR risk the displeasure of the US by refusing the passage of American warships, as it refused the U-2 flights?

gious power is not concentrated, and Turkey is basically a secular state.

During the past decade, Turkey has been developing its own slightly nervous, slightly tongue-in-cheek ostpolitik, a rapprochement with the Soviet Union and her allies, partly as a process of improving security through easing regional tensions, partly to pick up additional trade and aid[20] to supplement the greater quantity available from the West, and partly (one must assume) to induce concessions from its NATO partners and the European Community. It has been modestly successful on all counts but Turkey is still a long way from solvency or stability.

Western powers fear that because of its political instability and ambivalence, economic weakness and susceptibility to terrorism, Turkey will not have the cohesive strength to act firmly in a crisis involving NATO. But a greater fear stems from Turkey's quarrels with Greece. These have a history going back several centuries with many forced exchanges of territory. The two principal contemporary aspects are the conflicting claims to sovereignty in the Aegean with respect to territorial waters, the continental shelf, ownership of islands, and air space; and the dispute over Cyprus. Allegedly valuable oil and mineral deposits are at stake, exacerbating the problem. Greece claims virtually the whole of the Aegean Sea, and has put military forces on several of the disputed islands in contravention of the Treaty of Lausanne, 1923, and the Treaty of Paris, 1947. If Greece and then Turkey were to extend their territorial waters to twelve miles, the Greek share of the Aegean would be 69% and the Turkish 10%, and all ships sailing from major Turkish ports into the Mediterranean would have to pass through Greek territorial waters. Turkey has said that it would regard such an extension as a *casus belli*.[21]

Cyprus in the eastern Mediterranean close to Turkey offers a confrontation at one remove, complicated by the British bases in the southern (Greek) part of the island. Successive Greek governments have wanted to bring Cyprus under Greek sovereignty, and part of the Cyprus campaign for independence against Britain was waged by Greek Cypriots with Greek support and with this objective (*enosis*, or union, with Greece). The island's population is 78% Greek and 18% Turkish, and the two groups co-existed uneasily after independence in 1960 under a largely Greek Cypriot administration headed by Achbishop Makarios. In July 1974 the military government in Athens promoted a coup against Makarios, whereupon Turkish forces invaded the island and occupied more than a third of it in order to protect the Turkish community. They expelled Greek Cypriots from the occupied area. These events helped promote the return to democracy in Greece, but the new Greek government, offended by the action of a NATO power which NATO did not restrain, withdrew from the NATO integrated military structure. The US government imposed an arms embargo on Turkey, which then 'suspended' 25 American bases in Turkey[22] including five connected with monitoring the Strategic Arms Limitation agreements.

Seven years later, the Cyprus deadlock appears no closer to being broken, but there has been some movement in the Turkish-US relationship, despite the best efforts of the US Congress to keep it sour. In late 1978 the arms embargo was lifted and an electronic listening post at Sinop on the Black Sea, and a radar station at Pirinclik near Diyarbakir in south-eastern Turkey, were reactivated. Others followed, on changed conditions which included greater Turkish participation. These developments, plus massive Western aid given on the condition of vigorous and inevitably unpopular domestic economic constraints, have left Turkey an ambivalent member of the alliance. American U-2 aircraft used for SALT monitoring have had to be transferred to one of the British sovereign bases in Cyprus and the Turkish government has even decided not to permit the aircraft to fly over Turkish territory unless the Soviet Union gives its consent. This curious condition imposed by an ally on behalf of a potential enemy, coming at a time when US bases in Iran were abandoned, presumably has its origin in three converging pressures: 1 from the Soviet Union upon Turkey, which has a strategic vested interest; which offers diplomatic support against Greece; and which (with Bulgaria) is supplying Turkey with increasing quantities of electrical power and has even contracted to build a nuclear power station in Turkey; 2 from the Turkish government upon the West as a bargaining lever in trying to get the best terms for economic aid; and 3 from Turkish *amour propre* which objects to being either a mendicant to one superpower or a pawn between the two of them. Turkey also effectively blocked for a time attempts by Greece to return to the NATO fold on the old conditions. Left-wing groups in Cyprus continue their campaign to close the British sovereign bases there.

All this adds up to very much less than a solid NATO front against any possible attempts by the Soviet Union to use its power in a crisis in the region, such as an attempt to force Yugoslavia — or even indeed Albania — back into the Soviet fold. Both Greece and Turkey have satisfactory relations with the USSR[23] and with Soviet bloc states yet both offer political and psychological barriers to the extension of Soviet power. In military terms, Turkey provides significant armed forces, sits astride a vital strategic waterway, must be considered a possible constraint upon any Soviet ambitions in Iran, and (with, to a lesser extent, Greece) offers facilities highly important to Western navies in the Mediterranean and to American global defence capacity. It is that capacity expressed through NATO that gives both Greece and Turkey their ultimate protection. NATO needs them but in an unstable world they could well need NATO more. One can but hope that should the alliance ever require them they will be able to set aside their historic quarrels and mutual animosities, but present indications are that their fear of the Soviet Union is less powerful than their suspicion and dislike of each other. It would depend on the circumstances whether this would change in the event of a new Soviet bid for territory or power in their vicinity.

Yugoslavia

For over 30 years, Yugoslavia under Tito managed to preserve a somewhat precarious, tilted, but recognised independence between the Eastern and Western blocs. This was due primarily to the way in which it emerged from World War II, with a regime which had fought effectively, quickly established control over the whole country, owed little to the Soviet Union, and had a strong sense of nationalism, independence and toughness. It was due to the facts of geography — Yugoslavia does not share a border with the Soviet Union, it has a long and open coastline on the Adriatic (making outside reinforcement possible), and mountainous terrain suitable for guerrilla warfare in which Yugoslav partisans had developed considerable expertise. It was due also to the rigid, hamhanded authoritarianism of both Stalin and Khrushchev, who tried to force Tito and the Yugoslav government into a more subservient relationship than — despite their political proclivities — they were prepared to accept.

Yugoslavia has been helped by the readiness of the West, and especially of the United States, to support it in its assertion of sovereignty through economic and military aid and trade so that Tito felt more confident, from time to time, in asserting his independence from Moscow, and Moscow could never be certain of the extent to which the West would aid Yugoslavia in the event of an attempted Soviet takeover.

Finally, Yugoslav independence has been promoted by the wider milieu Tito found for it, the international status he built up over the years as a vigorous independent state, and a leader of the Non-Aligned Movement (NAM) a sizable group of nations who did not want to be dominated by either superpower. Although wielding litthe real political clout, the NAM has become respected to a degree by both superpowers, and has given Yugoslavia a cushion against the undue influence of either.

With the ending of Tito's control over his country, it is widely assumed that the Soviet Union will be particularly watchful for opportunities to ensure, one way or another, that Yugoslavia becomes part of the Soviet bloc. Tito himself long feared that this would occur, and repeatedly tried to obtain credible assurances from Soviet leaders that they would not force the issue.[24] This in itself must have been cause for alarm in Belgrade. When Tito became ill in January 1980, the armed forces went on alert as a demonstrative precaution against Soviet (or any other) meddling in Yugoslav affairs.[25] The state of readiness continued after his death. Although most informed opinion seems to consider such an invasion most unlikely, informed opinion has been known to be wrong on crucial issues.

What does the USSR want of Yugoslavia? We do not know the minds of the Soviet leaders, or who among them during their own change of leadership is or will emerge as dominant, or what will be the circumstances in Yugoslavia of which the Soviet government may wish to take advantage, or what would be the reactions of Hungary, Romania or Bulgaria if the Soviets were to decide to force the issue by military means.[26]

Notwithstanding these accumulated uncertainties, if a Yugoslav government were to shift or be shifted to a relationship with the Soviet Union of a nature somewhere between that of Bulgaria and Romania, i.e. between enthusiastic endorsement of Soviet foreign policies and reluctant acquiescence in most of them, this would be an immense gain to the Soviet Union. Yugoslavia would have been brought at last, with its sovereignty limited, into the 'Socialist Commonwealth' pronounced by Brezhnev in 1968. Its long defiance of Moscow would be demonstrated as ultimately ineffectual. A body blow would have been struck at the whole concept of there being different roads to socialism. Presumably Yugoslav port facilities would be more freely available to Soviet naval vessels and denied to the West's,[27] thus affecting the naval balance in the Adriatic and eastern Mediterranean. There would have to be extensive restructuring of the Yugoslav economy. The West's capacity to engage in political dialogue with Yugoslavia would be reduced. The NAM, already without its principal spokesman, would lose its most effective exponent.[28] A much more rigid regime would be imposed on the Yugoslav country and people. Warsaw Pact forces on Yugoslav territory would pose a threat to neighbouring NATO countries (Greece and Turkey). Albania would feel in line for a takeover. The capacity of the West to exert influence in the Balkan area would be significantly reduced. There would be a greater East-West polarisation, with the East stronger and the West weaker.

Any Soviet government would welcome such a turn of events if it could be achieved at an acceptable cost. On the basis of Soviet policies since 1945, we must assume that now Tito is dead the USSR will hope to be able to make some moves in this direction. They could range from gentle diplomatic pressures to a massive military assault.[29]

Cet animal est dangereux

There is no doubt that there would be considerable cost to the USSR if it used force. There has been little overt support in Yugoslavia for a close relationship with the Soviet Union and such support as has appeared at times was ruthlessly suppressed by Tito. The Yugoslav government has repeatedly declared that the country will fight any invader, and the armed forces (the Yugoslav People's Army, or YPA) is geared to do so. There is widespread antagonism towards the USSR by both leaders and people. The terrain favours the defender much more than the attacker.

The YPA has always been both a military and a political force in the country; its military commanders are members of the party hierarchy. It is a powerful force for cohesion throughout Yugoslavia, and should be a strong stabilising element in the transition to a post-Tito leadership and system. Its ethnic and regional composition roughly parallels that of the population, except that around two-thirds of the officer corps are Serbs. Its loyalty to Tito has never been questioned, but its loyalty to Tito's successors, especially if they quarrel among themselves or if the army is called upon to suppress 'nationalist' outbreaks,[30] is an unknown quantity. An external attack or threat would presumably have a unifying effect on the country but in the unlikely event of the country being already divided into warring factions it is conceivable that one of them might seek external military assistance.

The defence system of Yugoslavia was reorganised after the Soviet invasion of Czechoslovakia in 1968. There is a small, well-armed regular navy, and a small air force with about 350 combat aircraft. The main deterrent is in the army of about 190 000[31] (including 130 000 conscripts), plus a territorial defence force (variously reported at between 1 and 3 million) and a civil defence force. Declared policy is not to yield any Yugoslav territory to a foreign power. In fact, the Yugoslav army could not possibly defend itself on its own against a major Soviet assault, and the strategy is that it would withdraw, fighting, to the mountains from which it would wage a guerrilla war. Arms and arms factories are accordingly located throughout the country to meet this contingency.

The casualties of a guerrilla war — perhaps indefinitely protracted — would be part of the cost of a Soviet invasion, but they would not prevent or significantly reduce Soviet occupation of the country. Although Yugoslavia claims to be 80% self-sufficient in arms, foreign observers say the YPA has a wide variety of types of weapons, with all the consequent problems of repairs, replacements, compatibility, etc. Some of them are obsolete or obsolescent. The ability of regular and territorial forces to operate together in combat conditions has yet to be demonstrated. An occupying power would dominate communications and the Yugoslav forces would have to operate under decentralised command and control systems, as in World War II, but perhaps without the vital external support. In the event that the various national groups became concerned with their mutual hostilities, the fact that they are armed might only exacerbate their differences and increase the penalties therefor.

The ethnic composition of the Yugoslav population is the most complex and volatile in Europe (see Table 14). The use of the term 'nationality' for each of them is not an over-statement. These are people with an intense sense of common group identity formed over centuries of determined self-protection against adjacent groups and within a basically foreign imperial dominance. Brought together in their present form at the end of World War I following the dissolution of the Austro-Hungarian and Ottoman empires, their allegiance to 'Yugoslavia' is relatively recent. It has been largely forged under a communist dictatorship (initially dominated by Serbs and Montenegrins) which found itself compelled to make regional political and economic concessions of many kinds. Just as in external affairs Tito veered between pro-Soviet and anti-Soviet positions, so in domestic policies he veered between an authoritarian centralism and a more liberal, grass-roots regionalism. And although he made sure that federal (i.e. Yugoslav) interests prevailed and dissent was contained, the system he evolved entrenched ethnic and regional interests at all levels and demanded strong leadership at the centre.

All the minorities have international affiliations or are the subject of irredentist claims or pressures. This is especially the case with the Macedonians over whom authority is periodically claimed by Bulgaria and who also have links with Greece; with the Albanians of Kosovo who have an Albanian flag and language; with the (Sunni) Muslim Nationals of Bosnia-Hercegovina who have shown an interest in other Islamic communities, and with the Croatians, who have sizable and intensely nationalistic expatriate communities in the United States, Australia and elsewhere. By variations of repression and concession, Tito managed to fuse each of these groups more solidly into the Yugoslav state, but such processes are necessarily slow.

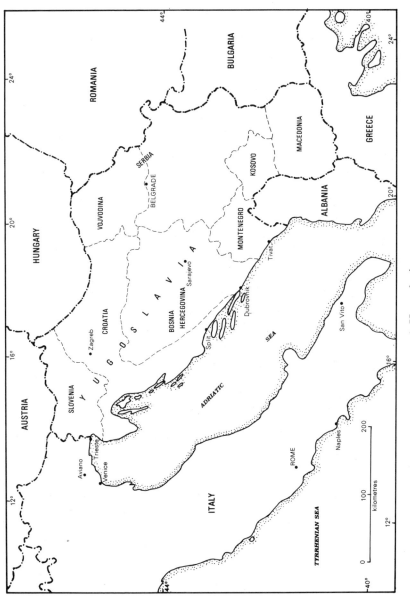

4 Yugoslavia

Although demonstrating an unusual longevity, Tito realised that he would not always be there to encourage or coerce his subordinates into putting Yugoslavia first. Various organisational experiments produced the present situation whereby there is a collective State Presidency of 9 persons representing the 6 republics and 2 provinces plus the president of the Presidium, and a 23-member Presidium in which ultimate authority lies. The chairmen of both bodies rotate annually. It is hard to see this system surviving for very long. Not only does it lack Tito's authority, but a rotating chairman is not conducive to stability. The Presidium is substantially of the Partisan generation and will be subject to pressures from below which Tito was able to contain. Its authority is diffused by being effected through eight Commissions and by the budgetary powers of the republics. Senior Party officials at the Federal and Republic levels have been Tito's men, holding office by his grace or favour: they too will be under pressure. The system of rotating public servants between different parts of the administration was so inconvenient that it has required a strong discipline to maintain, although it seems to have worked well enough in a society where 'elections' are pre-arranged. As in other federations, economic differences between the regions are not adjusted by the federal system to everyone's satisfaction.

External and internal economic problems are a continuing cause for concern. Reacting to pressures from the republics, Tito's government made a great number of ad hoc decisions in principle and practice that left the economic system a mix of the features of both a planned economy and a market economy. The federal government has only occasionally been able to impose on the republics a single economic policy and the notion of a national market. Transfer of resources from the richer to the poorer areas has been resisted by the former, to the resentment of the latter. Local pressures have forced the creation of uneconomic industries in inappropriate areas.

So long as the economies of Western countries were buoyant and their export prices stable, Yugoslavs enjoyed a comparatively high standard of living. Nearly a million Yugoslavs working in Western Europe remitted hard currency home; European firms invested in Yugoslav industry and provided capital goods and credits to support Yugoslav expansion. But the international slow-down after 1973 hit Yugoslavia hard. The European community took fewer Yugoslav products, it repatriated a quarter to half of the immigrant workers; its exports cost more. 'Overheated' demand in Yugoslavia gave an extra push to inflation, whose problems were compounded by growing unemployment. Although half of Yugoslavia's foreign trade is with the West and a third with the Soviet bloc, only the latter will take payments in soft currency or by barter arrangements. Only the Soviet Union, with its vast, under-supplied consumer markets, can take the produce of inefficient Yugoslav factories. Half of Yugoslavia's oil imports are supplied by the Soviet Union at a time when the latter is beginning to curb the oil imports of its Warsaw Pact partners, when OPEC (which supplies most of the balance) keeps increasing oil prices, and when Yugoslav demand for oil is increasing because of industrial growth and a greater use of motor cars. The risen and still rising economic expectations of the Yugoslav consumer will be increasingly difficult to satisfy and this may cause political unrest.

The passing of Tito does not seem to have reduced authority at the centre, which might have been expected. Yet it could still happen as Western governments and investors wait to see how the country manages without a strong, charismatic leader, as the federal authorities find national remedies more difficult to impose, and as the republics continue to be unable to control a dangerously high level of inflation.

All this does not mean that the country will inevitably collapse upon itself or into the arms of the Soviet Union. Indeed, close observers of the Yugoslav scene tend to believe that most Yugoslavs support the present system and have no propensity to change it significantly; that the republic and national leaders are immensely conscious of the penalities of not 'hanging together'. There is widespread fear of and hostility to the Soviet Union. While the reins may loosen, and the incipient collective leadership may concede a degree of power to a single figure, general authority is not going to shift away from the League of Communists of Yugoslavia. The greater the sense of external threat, the greater will be the pressures for cohesion, and the greater the prestige and role of the YPA which is the one supra-regional or supra-national force.

Soviet incentives and constraints

Then why is Yugoslavia, in terms of the East-West balance, an area of potential danger? First, because Yugoslavia would be such a rich prize for the Soviet Union — ideologically, psychologically, and especially strategically. There is thus a strong incentive for the Soviet government to take advantage of uncertainties in leadership and problems in cohesion. Secondly, because we have been talking not about facts but about probabilities, and even such expert opinion as believes that Yugoslavia will hold together concedes that this is a probability for a relatively short period of years, and the degree of estimated probability seems to range from about 50–60%. Thirdly, because although the Western powers would provide aid of various kinds, they have shown no great enthusiasm for coming actively to the defence of Yugoslavia and so perhaps risking global war.[32] During the Carter administration, the United States appeared a less credible balance to the USSR than a few years before. This may change under Reagan — we will have to wait and see. And finally, because the Russians could invade the country with relative ease through Hungary and Bulgaria, or (less easily) through Romania or from the sea.[33]

What are the deterrents to or constraints on Soviet action? Despite what the invasion of Afghanistan may suggest, the USSR has a natural reluctance to embark on war, especially war against a determined enemy. World opinion, to which Moscow pays some heed on occasions, would be strongly hostile. The effect on the West must be uncertain: the Soviets cannot be sure how it will react. The effects in Eastern Europe must equally be uncertain, and could conceivably lead to widespread, even bloc-shattering, eruptions, especially as Soviet control over the bloc has loosened somewhat in recent years and looming economic stresses could well weaken it even further. In any case, so long as the Soviet Union is involved in a sizable military operation in Afghanistan, with the widespread international opprobrium that has attracted, and is troubled by Polish liberalisation, it must feel some constraints on military activities elsewhere.

For these reasons, the Soviet government is much more likely to try diplomatic pressures and subversive means to ease the new Yugoslav leadership to a more accommodating line of policy, at least until a situation occurs within Yugoslavia (if it does) whereby there is a breakdown of internal security, and until the Soviet Union is given, as in Hungary, Czechoslovakia and Afghanistan, both a quasi-legal basis for intervening and a strong indication that it could be successful. Alternatively, if a post-Tito Yugoslav government looked like making a radical change away from its general communist alignment, such is the arrogance of Soviet power and its fear of the disintegration of the Soviet system that it might conceivably act first and count the cost afterwards.

Yet there is some awareness in the West that the fate of Yugoslavia is of a different order from the fate of Afghanistan. After two years of limp negotiations dominated by the negative attitudes of the French and the Irish, the European Community concluded a relatively favourable agreement for access of Yugoslav goods to EC markets. Simple geography makes it possible for the NATO powers to support, supply or reinforce Yugoslavia; simple self-interest should inform them that their greatest danger lies in acquiescing in Soviet imperialism on the continent of Europe.

Table 14   *Ethnic Composition of Yugoslavia as at 1971 Census*

	Percentage	
Slovenia (1.7 m) (1.8 m)*	94.0	Slovenes
	0.5	Hungarians
	0.2	Italians
Croatia (4.4 m) (4.6 m)	79.0	Croats
	14.0	Serbs
	1.0	Hungarians
	0.5	Italians
Bosnia and Hercegovina (3.7 m) (4.1 m)	40.0	Muslim nationals
	38.0	Serbs
	21.0	Croats
Serbia:		
Vojvodina (2 m) (2 m)	56.0	Serbs
	22.0	Hungarians
	7.0	Croats
Serbia proper (5.3 m) (5.5 m)	90.0	Serbs
	1.0	Muslim nationals
	1.0	Albanians
	1.0	Bulgarians
Kosovo (1.2 m) (1.5 m)	74.0	Albanians
	18.0	Serbs
Montenegro (0.5 m) (0.6 m)	68.0	Montenegrins
	13.0	Muslim nationals
	8.0	Serbs
	7.0	Albanians
Macedonia (1.6 m) (1.8 m)	70.0	Macedonians
	17.0	Albanians
Total Population (20.5 m) (22.0 m)	40.0	Serbs
	22.0	Croats
	8.0	Muslim nationals
	8.0	Slovenes
	6.0	Albanians
	6.0	Macedonians
	3.0	Montenegrins
	3.0	Hungarians
	1.0	Yugoslavs
	3.0	Other

* Figures in the second brackets are a recent estimate. *New York Times* 27 January 1980.

While events since Tito's death encourage the belief that Yugoslavia will be able to remain stable and viable, we cannot ignore the possibility that it will not do so. Internal tensions and conflict might, with judicious Soviet assistance, yield to the Soviet government all the political influence it desires without military action. In such circumstances, it would be much more difficult for the Western powers to intervene to safeguard Yugoslavia's political independence and territorial integrity.

Yugoslavia has long had observer status at CMEA and is a member of some of its groups. If the Yugoslav internal situation begins to deteriorate, the collective leadership might tighten party discipline and return to a more dogmatic economic doctrine less different from that of the Soviet Union and thus with less reason publicly to demonstrate its difference. This is a second-worse case (the worst being Soviet occupation), and it is more probable that the country will return to uneasy stability and sovereignty, avoiding with practised and prickly skill either the embrace or the hostility of both blocs.

NATO's Northern Flank

Norway is the smallest (other than Iceland) and most vulnerable of the NATO powers. It has a population of 4 million, a main coastline of over 21 000 km, and has borders with the Soviet Union, Finland and Sweden. On the short Soviet border, Norway has about a battalion facing roughly two Soviet divisions. Iceland, some 900 km off the Norwegian coast, has the direct protection of American forces, but Norway has no NATO army bases or forces permanently stationed there, although American, British, Canadian and Dutch forces, and a NATO mobile force, train regularly in Norway and military supplies are stockpiled and pre-positioned in the country. Norwegian forces take part in joint NATO exercises. No nuclear weapons are deployed on Norwegian soil.

In any Soviet-NATO battle for the Atlantic, the bases and communications facilities in Norway would be of immense importance to the Western alliance.

Partly because of the enclosed nature of the Baltic and Black seas, and the primacy of the Europe-Atlantic theatre, the Soviet Union's largest fleet, the Northern Fleet, operates from the Kola peninsula and the White Sea. It comprises 120 submarines and 80 major surface combat ships and includes 70% of the Soviet strategic nuclear missile-carrying submarines including all its Delta-II submarines armed with the SSN-8 missile. With the range of these missiles, the submarines do not need to leave the general area of the Barents and Greenlands seas (i.e. do not need to pass through the Iceland-Norway gap into the Atlantic) in order to strike America, although presumably some would want to in a time of tension. This area, including the Svalbard archipelago (sometimes known by its main island, Spitzbergen), is thus central to the East-West strategic balance. Soviet early warning systems are located on the Kola peninsula; there are also major air defence bases designed to protect the Soviet submarine fleet from NATO attack. This region is thus the core of the Soviet Union's second strike capability, and the Soviet government will do everything possible to protect it.

Norway is an essential link in NATO's defence intelligence and operational capacity. Seabed sonar stations between the Norwegian mainland and Svalbard monitor Soviet submarines in the region as well as all shipping passing through that gap to and from the Atlantic or the North Sea. Norway is host to NATO maritime reconnaissance aircraft and to AWACS airborne early warning systems. These are vital to the defence of Western naval merchant shipping.

If in situations short of war Norway is vital to NATO, in war Norway must be presumed vital to the Soviet Union: positively as providing (once occupied) the air bases for striking at NATO shipping, and negatively in that the Norwegian intelligence-gathering facilities would have to be put out of action as quickly as possible. Thus the degree of Soviet pressure on Norway is something of a barometer of Soviet general ambitions or assertiveness.

There is no doubt that Soviet pressures have increased disturbingly in recent years, with merchant-intelligence vessels violating Norwegian territorial waters and aircraft entering Norwegian air space, presumably to probe the electronic defences. Soviet nuclear submarines now operate openly in the Baltic Sea, contravening a long-standing if tacit agreement between the Soviet and Scandinavian governments. Perhaps the most unpleasant pressures have been directed against Svalbard, over which Norway was accorded sovereignty by an international treaty in February 1920. The USSR adhered to the Treaty in 1935 and there are 40 other contractual signatories, including all the 'Great Powers'.

The Svalbard Treaty granted Norway 'full and absolute sovereignty' over Svalbard but also laid down that nationals of all the contracting parties are entitled, on a basis of equality, to carry on various types of economic activity such as mining, fishing, hunting, and commercial dealings. There are constraints on military activities, in that no permanent defence installations are permitted under the Treaty.

In 1944, the Soviet Foreign Minister, Molotov, proposed that the Svalbard Treaty be declared invalid, the southern-most island of the group be handed over to the Soviet Union, and the rest of the archipelago be made subject to joint Norwegian-Soviet rule. The Norwegian government-in-exile rejected the request, but felt compelled to agree that the defence of Svalbard should be viewed as a joint responsibility of the two states, provided the Norwegian Storting (parliament) agreed. The Storting, under the impact of the early post-war changing strategic situation, did not agree. When Norway joined NATO in April 1949, Svalbard became part of the NATO area, though against Soviet protests; it was not fortified. More recently (1976–77) Norway established a 200 km economic zone off the mainland and a fishing protection zone round Svalbard, the legality of which the USSR has contested. There is now an ongoing dispute between the two countries over a series of maritime issues, including fishing, sovereignty over the Norwegian continental shelf, and the delimitation line in the Barents Sea. Expectation of oil and gas finds in the Svalbard-Barents Sea area has not made these problems any easier of solution. The USSR is the only other government involved or interested in exploiting the maritime resources.

Two recent incidents have marred Norwegian-Soviet relations over Svalbard. The first was the erection, without consulting Norway, of a Soviet radar installation at the helicopter station on Cape Heer. The second was the crash of a Soviet military aircraft on the island of Hopen (when it had no business to be in the area) and the subsequent dispute over its 'black box'. The USSR came close to making military threats. In general, the Soviet government seems to be deliberately eroding the practice and principle of Norwegian sovereignty over Svalbard.

This is thus an area of potential danger to the East-West balance because of Norway's strategic importance to NATO, its physical weakness, its disputes with the Soviet Union over territory, boundaries and resources, the importance of the Barents-Greenland Seas to Soviet strategic and tactical defensive and offensive capacity, and the growing Soviet pressures for military superiority. Norway's judicious combination of firmness on principle and flexibility in practice, of physical resistance and diplomatic negotiations, backed by its NATO membership, has protected it from excessive Soviet demands; but it treads a delicate path. Sweden, for so long a neutral power acting on the basis of armed self-reliance, has found the costs of the policy increasingly exhorbitant as Soviet pressures harden. The main Swedish air bases would be most valuable to the USSR in the event of operations against Norway, or to provide air cover in breaking out into the Atlantic. Sweden accordingly is moving closer to the West, in an unspoken (and one hopes not misplaced) reliance on NATO as its ultimate defence. Finland, on the other hand, is considerably and unavoidably more deferential to its giant Soviet neighbour.

A direct attack on Norway would unambiguously be a direct attack on NATO. What we are seeing instead is a slow but steady pressure to whittle away Norway's value to the Western alliance, in an attempt to achieve by degrees and without ringing alarm bells some of the important advantages of occupation without paying the price.

These circumstances point to a troubling of the Nordic balance, in which there is close if tacit defence co-operation among the five Nordic partners, and a new degree of tension, a greater fragility, along NATO's least-protected, least protectable flank.

6   AREAS OF STRATEGIC COMPETITION

Africa and the Indian Ocean

There has so far been no direct confrontation in Africa between the Soviet Union and the United States. This is primarily because Africa has been the subject of European rather than of American imperialist ventures, and has been geographically and psychologically too removed from obvious US national interests. With the one exception of Liberia, the states of Africa have all been colonies of one or another European power — the UK, France, Belgium, Italy, Spain or Portugal. None of the imperial powers prepared their black African colonies adequately for independence. None was able to establish the basis for lasting democratic government. Few created an efficient and effective bureaucracy. In very few has the army remained independent of politics. Boundaries between states were drawn arbitrarily by the metropolitan power, often irrationally dividing tribes or 'nationalities'. Trade and communications were largely with the imperial country, and not with neighbours. Economic development of benefit to the indigenes was scattered and limited, so that their average per capita income is still only about $200 per year. Competing European cultures were laid over a vastly more numerous range of traditional languages, beliefs, systems and loyalties. It is not surprising therefore that the states of Africa which became independent between 1957 and 1980 have had so many problems, so much internal instability, so much resentment against their real or imagined colonial and racial humiliations; that they have made repeated demands for retribution and recognition; and that many of them, seeing the US as another Western imperial power, have turned willingly to the communist world (or worlds) to improve their standard of living, their physical security, their international status and their influence.

So far as one can tell, there are probably between 2 000 and 3 000 Soviet military advisers in Africa (see Table 15), some 40 000 Cuban combat troops and advisers, and Soviet, Cuban and East

European (especially East German) instructors have trained and helped guerrillas operating into Namibia, Zimbabwe, and South Africa. There is a very substantial Soviet or Soviet-Cuban military presence in Angola and Ethiopia, a significant presence in Benin, Cape Verde, Congo, Equatorial Guinea, Guinea, Guinea Bissau, Madagascar, Mali, Mozambique, Tanzania, and Zambia and a small presence in Burundi, Chad, Nigeria, Sao Tome-Principe, Sierra Leone, Comoros, Seychelles, Libya and Algeria — a total of 22 of the 49 non-white African states. The USSR has access to naval and air facilities in Ethiopia (Massawa, Assab, and the Dahlak Islands where there is a dry dock), South Yemen (Aden and Socotra), and Angola (Luanda). The United States has provided extensive economic and technical aid to many countries in Africa, some military aid, and under recent agreements has access to Mombasa in Kenya, to Mogadiscio in Somalia, and to facilities in Egypt. It could not be said that any part of Africa, except perhaps Egypt at present, is in an American sphere of influence. France retains use of the strategic port of Djibouti, and is influential in several of its former colonies, at times intervening with troops to support or even remove (as in the Central African Empire) a national leader.[1] In Chad, Zaire, Ivory Coast, Senegal, Mauritania and Morocco, France has intervened to protect its own interests and counter Soviet, Cuban or Libyan influence.

Soviet and Soviet bloc assistance to or intervention in black African states has responded to or taken advantage of the demands and resentments expressed by the emerging independent states, or of their desire to play East and West off against each other (e.g. Zambia's large arms deal with the USSR in 1980 despite a considerable aid programme from the West). The Soviet Union's objectives have been to increase its political influence at the expense of the West and (since the early 1960s) China, and to obtain facilities from which to project military power throughout the region. Some commentators believe the USSR also wants to obtain access to some of the more important mineral resources of (or off) the continent (see Table 16), even though there are few that they do not have already. It is much more plausible that they should wish to deny Africa's strategic materials to the Western powers that depend on them. The Soviets have had some success with African governments because they came bearing gifts (usually arms) and because, with the exception of France and, for a time, Portugal, the Western imperial powers had limited and selective residual interest in their former black African colonies.

There is a tendency in some Western circles, and in South Africa, to place great emphasis on the strategic significance of Soviet activities in Africa.[2] These are not easy judgements to make, but it is just

Table 15 *Estimate of Soviet Bloc Personnel in Sub-Saharan Africa, December 1979*

	Military advisers			Civilians		
	Soviet	Cuban	East European	Soviet	Cuban	East European
Angola	500 plus	19 000 mostly combat troops	300–350	350	6 500	700
Benin	30	Up to 50	—	10	—	5
Burundi	20	—	—	—	—	25
Cameroons	—	—	—	15	—	10
Cape Verde Islands	10	—	—	15	5	5
Central African Empire	—	—	—	50	—	45
Chad	Up to 50	—	—	25	—	—
Congo	30	Up to 300	30	150	75	90
Equatorial Guinea	Up to 100	200	—	40	50	—
Ethiopia	1 000 plus	15 000 mostly combat troops	150	200	450	175
Gabon	—	—	—	—	—	20
Gambia	—	—	—	10	—	—
Ghana	—	—	—	85	—	70
Guinea (Conakry)	25	350	—	300	50	120
Guinea Bissau	—	50–100	—	40	30	35
Ivory Coast	—	—	—	15	—	10

Kenya	—	—	—	10	—	35
Liberia	15	Up to 50	—	—	—	15
Madagascar	100–150	Up to 50	—	65	—	—
Mali	—	—	—	200	—	20
Mauritania	200	—	—	50	—	—
Mozambique	—	200	100	290	600	325
Niger	Up to 100	—	—	—	—	5
Nigeria	—	Up to 50	20	1 000	—	525
Sao Tome-Principe	—	—	—	—	100	10
Senegal	—	Up to 50	—	10	—	30
Sierra Leone	150–200	—	—	20	—	—
Somalia	—	Up to 50	10	—	—	10
Tanzania	Up to 150	—	—	100	150	80
Togo	—	—	10	—	—	65
Uganda	—	—	—	35	—	—
Zaire	—	—	—	—	—	250
Zambia	25 (ZNDF and ZAPU)	Up to 100 (with ZAPU)	30–40 ZAPU	125	—	55

Source: Various, especially UK Foreign and Commonwealth Office Background Briefs and reference papers (unclassified).

Table 16   *The Importance of Southern Africa to World Minerals Supply, 1977**

Mineral	Share of non-communist output, %	Share of world output, %	Major producers (share of world output except for uranium oxide) %
Antimony	26	17	Bolivia (22), China (17), South Africa (17), USSR (11)
Asbestos	24	12	USSR (46), Canada (29), South Africa (7), Rhodesia (Zimbabwe) (4), China (4) South Africa (34), USSR (22), Albania, (9), Turkey (6),
Chromite	61	42	Rhodesia (Zimbabwe) (6), Finland (6)
Cobalt*	50	44	Zaire (36), New Caledonia (14), Australia (12), Zambia (8), USSR (6)
Copper	23	18	USA (17), USSR (14), Chile (13), Canada (10), Zambia (8), Zaire (6)
Gem diamonds (natural)	87	69	South Africa (37), USSR (20), Namibia (18)
Industrial diamonds (natural)	84	60	Zaire (37), USSR (28), South Africa (14), Botswana (8)
Gold	75	59	South Africa (57), USSR (20)
Manganese ore	41	23	USSR (39), South Africa (23), Gabon (8), India (8), Australia (6)

Table 16 *The Importance of Southern Africa to World Minerals Supply, 1977* (cont.)*

Mineral	Share of non-communist output, %	Share of world output, %	Major producers (share of world output except for uranium oxide) %
Platinum-group metals	85	46	South Africa (46), USSR (45), Canada (8)
Uranium oxide (U_3O_8) concentrate	22	?	USA (39), Canada (20), South Africa (11), Namibia (10), (communist countries: not known)
Vanadium	57	40	South Africa (37), USSR (30), USA (20)

* Based on production data which are partly estimated and in some instances incomplete.

Sources: US Bureau of Mines, *Mineral Trade Notes*, various issues; *Copper*, World Bureau of Metal Statistics, *World Metal Statistics*, January 1979.

as unfortunate to exaggerate as to underestimate the strength and implications of communist influence. Soviet and Soviet-sponsored operations in Africa have been selective, limited, and only partially successful. Soviet economic aid accounts for probably less than 3% of all aid to Africa, and trade no more than 2%. Soviet economic aid is rarely able to satisfy the demands made of it, and this has been the case in African claimant states. The result has been that most African states have resorted to the West for the greater part of their economic and technical needs, using multi-national institutions as well as the resources of the former imperial rulers, the US, Germany and Japan. Francophone and subsequently other African states obtained an advantageous relationship with the European Community through the Yaoundé and subsequently the Lomé conventions. Soviet military aid has been useful to revolutionary movements, but most states feel that they have concluded their own revolution. Soviet aid to governments has often had ideological strings sticking out of the parcel, and especially the notion of creating a political system compatible with the inculcation of Soviet Marxist doctrine. But left-leaning regimes (such as in Mozambique, Ethiopia, Zambia) have not proved receptive to the idea of creating, on Soviet demand, mass Marxist political parties as the base and channel of their authority, presumably because they see such parties as a possible challenge to that authority and in any case cutting across the tribal system which is usually the basis of society and the source of power. Perhaps they resist it also because they see it as a means for imposing Soviet authority which, however useful, is indisputably alien.

While acknowledging and sometimes falling foul of the complexity and arbitrariness of African politics, the Soviet government, in the areas where it has been effective, has undoubtedly moved the strategic balance there significantly in its favour, at least for a time. It has brought important parts of the continent into its sphere of influence, using proxy forces (mostly Cubans) to bear the burden of any fighting and to deflect from itself the resentment and political backlash which external military intervention can always generate.

Yet even where the Soviet Union has a clear advantage over rival external influences, the situation is never straightforward, or never stays straightforward for long — such is the nature of Africa. The Soviet experience with Egypt is perhaps the best example. The USSR became Egypt's principal source of economic and military aid following the 1956 Western decision not to finance the Aswan Dam, and the subsequent nationalisation of the Canal and the Anglo-French-Israeli invasion of Egypt. The Soviet Union provided the arms for Egypt again prior to the six-day war of 1967, and for the October 1973 war, following a Treaty of Friendship and Co-operation (including security) in 1971. Yet twice the Egyptian government, determined to be its own master, has sent Soviet advisers home; it abrogated the Treaty in March 1976, and now has a strong military partnership with the United States which — so long as it lasts — must act as a constraint on any Soviet military activities in the region. Egypt is not the only country to reject Soviet aid. A Soviet-supported coup in the Sudan misfired and Soviet advisers were thrown out of Somalia (see below).

External interests

The external powers are interested in the African states for two principal reasons: mineral deposits and geo-strategic advantage. Apart from oil (especially in Libya, Algeria and Nigeria), the main strategic minerals are in southern Africa (see Table 16) and especially in South Africa which is the world's largest producer of chromite (an essential component of stainless steel), gem diamonds, gold, platinum-group metals and vanadium (an important ingredient of speciality steels). South Africa is the largest non-communist producer of manganese, an essential ingredient in steel-making, for

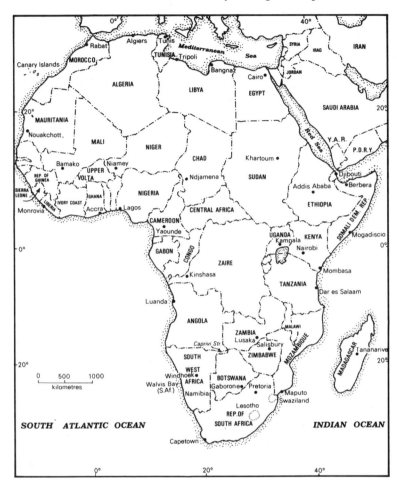

5 Africa

which there is no substitute. It is an important supplier of antimony, asbestos, industrial diamonds and uranium (half being located in Namibia). Zaire is the world's largest producer of cobalt and of industrial diamonds. Zimbabwe is a useful producer of chromite. The Western powers are heavily dependent on southern Africa, and particularly on South Africa, for the continuing supply of these items. Interruption to supplies would not only send up prices, it would also be industrially and strategically disadvantageous.

Each part of Africa has its own strategic circumstances and considerations. Basically, ports on the north African coast could be extremely important in the event of East-West conflict in the Mediterranean. The Suez-Red Sea passage, so easily blockable, is still a major commercial waterway; it cuts several thousand kilometres off the journey from the Black Sea or the Mediterranean to the northern or eastern Indian Ocean; its adjacent lands border the Middle East oil-producing states. Other coastal facilities affect the strategic situation in the south Atlantic and western Indian Oceans.

Involvement by external powers has led them into complex and shifting situations. In North Africa, for example, Algeria is a major recipient of Soviet arms aid and has the tacit support of the Soviet Union in its dispute with Morocco and Mauritania over the Western (formerly Spanish) Sahara. Yet Morocco is the largest single recipient of Soviet economic aid, having been given a loan of $2 billion for exploitation of the Meskala phosphate deposits which fortuitously include a significant proportion of uranium. Relations between Morocco (supported by the United States) and Mauritania (supported by France) are periodically tense. Mauritania also receives aid from China, Romania, and several Arab states. Libya, with a population of less than three million, has arms agreements with communist countries to a total of $3.6 billion, and Tripoli (Tarabulus) is the most powerful arsenal of Soviet bloc arms outside the Warsaw Pact, posing a continuing threat to Egypt (which also for many years received Soviet arms aid) and to NATO's Mediterranean fleet. Libya unsuccessfully tried to establish facilities in Malta. It has involved itself with the Chad civil war, expropriated a strip of uranium-bearing territory, and declared a union of the two countries. The USSR is building a nuclear power plant and a research reactor in Libya which has an erratic and volatile dictatorship, and the Soviets are also exploring for more oil and for uranium. Libya strongly supports Arab extremism and terrorism generally. The Polisario Front, trying to carve its own territory out of the Western Sahara, is armed (with Soviet arms) and supplied by Algeria and Libya. The effects of the instability of these situations are mitigated by the great distances involved, and by their own changing character.

Sometimes the situation gets almost ludicrously cosmopolitan. In Bujumbura, the capital of the tiny central African republic of Burundi, for example, a *New York Times* reporter in mid-1980 wrote that the North Koreans were building the president a new palace, the Cubans were training fighter pilots for an as yet non-existent air force, Soviet military hardware was on display in the capital and the Chinese had just opened a textile mill.[3] Yet the taking of offence by a political leader, or a successful coup (these average about three per year in Africa) against him can change an orientation from China to the USSR or from the USSR to the United States or to non-alignment. In the guerilla war against the Muzorewa government in Zimbabwe/Rhodesia, one part of the Patriotic Front (led by Joshua Nkomo) was supported by the Soviet Union and East Germany, the other (led by Robert Mugabe) by China, Yugoslavia and Romania (see below).

East Germany's limited aid has been distributed to selective targets apparently under an overall Soviet programme, especially in Angola, Mozambique and in Ethiopia where it has helped train the people's militia. It has concentrated on military assistance, mainly in the fields of intelligence and security. In some places such as Somalia and Egypt it has been able to keep a diplomatic and aid presence after Soviet and Cuban representatives have been expelled. Western reports indicate that there are currently about 4 000 East German civilian and military personnel working in Africa.

The Chinese People's Republic has used selected African countries as the main beneficiaries of an aid programme designed to counter Soviet influence in the region. Aid has been given mainly for projects concerned with agricultural development, road building, the construction of railways, ports, public buildings, light industrial plant and food processing. The largest project was the Tanzam railway (between Tanzania and Zambia) completed in 1976; significant aid also has been given to the Sudan and to Zaire, as well as arms aid to Zambia. Although well received, Chinese aid seems to have had little effect on the Soviet position in the region (the USSR has so much more to offer), although it has been affected by the Soviet position. China's relations with Ethiopia, for example, have deteriorated in recent years while those with Somalia have improved. In a number of colonial countries (Angola, Zimbabwe/ Rhodesia, South-West Africa) and in South Africa, the revolutionary movement split with the Soviet Union supporting one part and China the other. In pursuit of its anti-Soviet policies, in Africa as elsewhere, China has effectively become an ally of the West. When disaffected Congolese with some outside help[4] attempted to take over the copper-rich Zaire province of Shabah (previously known as Katanga) in 1977, Morocco, France, Belgium, China and the United States co-operated to defeat the attempt and save the wholly unworthy government of President Mobutu.

Angola and Ethiopia

There are at present two areas of Soviet strength in Africa: Angola and Ethiopia. Both are unstable and ambiguous. When events in Lisbon in 1974 led to the dissolution of the Portuguese empire, the

Soviet Union took advantage of the help it had given to the revolutionary Popular Movement for the Liberation of Angola (MPLA) to reinforce the relationship and bring it to power. Angola had (and has) rich resources of oil, diamonds, iron, copper and other minerals. It has several ports well placed on the eastern Atlantic seaboard, especially Luanda. It is not an understatement to say that during 1975 the Soviet Union 'poured' arms into Angola, plus Soviet and Cuban advisers and Cuban combat personnel. While the timings of the several interventions have been variously reported, by August 1975 Cubans were engaged in fighting the two other indigenous liberation groups, the National Front for the Liberation of Angola (FNLA) and the National Union for the Total Independence of Angola (UNITA), all three having provisionally agreed earlier (before the Soviet arms aid to the MPLA) to combine to form an Angolan government. By late September 1975 Cuban forces began to arrive in substantial numbers.

The 'Western' response to these activities was tentative and disparate. During 1975 the United States and China provided limited aid to the FNLA and UNITA. South Africa, encouraged by Zambia, Zaire, and apparently also by the US, sent a force across the border in mid-October. It was a military success but it could not combat the increasingly superior Cuban forces or the international political opprobrium and domestic concern that the intervention aroused. In December the American Senate voted to stop all covert assistance to the FNLA and UNITA. During virtually the whole of the Soviet-Cuban build-up, the United States had not even bothered to protest against it. Dr Kissinger relied on the processes of detente he had so pragmatically built up but which he and the US Congress failed to see applied only to the areas where confronting military strength established a strategic balance.

Even with the help of about 20 000 Cuban military personnel, 1 000 Soviet advisers and some thousands of technicians imported from bloc countries, the MPLA has been unable to control more than about half of the country. President Neto, dissatisfied with this failure and troubled by the inevitable problems of foreigners in positions of political and military power, began to seek help in the West, and to look for a peaceful settlement to the Namibian dispute. In September 1979 Neto died under treatment in a Moscow hospital. The Soviets, Cubans and East Europeans remain, but their presence exacerbates the problems it is designed to eliminate. Although not exactly 'a Vietnam' for the USSR or Cuba, Angola has all the criteria of a foreign intervention bound ultimately to fail.

Yet Angola is one of the landmarks of the post-war strategic environment. The Soviet Union had supplied technicians and some pilots to Egypt, but in Angola for the first time it had provided combat troops to fight in a civil war outside the Soviet bloc (UNITA has reported also the capture of Soviet air force pilots). The fact that the troops were Cubans is both a plus and a minus for the Soviet government: a plus in that they deflect international opprobrium from the USSR, a minus in that their achievements are not credited to the USSR, and in some circumstances they may not be fully under Soviet control. They will also one day have to go home, and what then? Angola demonstrated Soviet capacity to airlift quickly across the world large quantities of arms and equipment and a division of troops. It demonstrated that where the Soviet government had the determination to take advantage of a revolutionary situation, the United States in a post-Vietnam phase was not prepared to counter such an initiative. It was the beginning of the considerable Soviet-Cuban military involvement on the continent of Africa.

Perhaps here one should consider the extent to which the Cubans are Soviet 'mercenaries' or reflect a specifically Cuban policy. Long before Angola, Cuba had expressed an interest in revolutionary situations in Africa, and it even made modest contributions. But to send 20 000 troops to Angola, and nearly the same number subsequently to Ethiopia, was not a modest contribution. To reinforce the notion that Cuba was acting on its own behalf President Castro developed a specifically Cuban foreign policy in Africa. He has visited sympathetic countries there and speaks and acts as if Cuba were taking its own decisions, giving its own aid, making its own sacrifices. This would all be more credible if there were the slightest possibility that Cuba could finance, arm, or transport its forces, but it cannot, and this is universally known. A policy without a capacity to carry it out is simply a state of mind, and while Castro's state of mind clearly suits the Soviet government very well, the Cubans in Africa are there at the expense and to fulfil the policies of the Soviet Union, although some of the costs are met by the host government, as is the case in Ethiopia.

Ethiopia is the second main Soviet involvement. Again the Soviet government took advantage of a revolutionary situation — the overthrow of Haile Selassie in 1974. Soviet support for and influence in Ethiopia increased after the assumption to power of Lieutenant-Colonel Haile Mariam Mengistu in February 1977. By late 1978 Ethiopia had $2 billion in military commitments from the Soviet Union plus $66 million from Eastern Europe. A series of arms agreements and a 20-year Treaty of Friendship and Co-operation were signed with the Soviet Union in 1977–78. American aid was dispensed with and the US communications facility at Asmara was closed.

Yet despite this diplomatic success, the Soviets entered here, as elsewhere in Africa, a scene they could not control. In 1969 the Soviet Union had begun an association with Somalia by which in a few years it became the largest supplier of arms and military advisers, expanded the air and naval facilities, and established a missile store for use by the Soviet naval squadron in the Indian Ocean. Presumably the USSR hoped to retain its influence in Somalia while expanding it in Ethiopia, but this underestimated Somalia's hostility to Ethiopia and its irredentist ambitions expressed also towards the Somali peoples in Kenya and the French territory of Djibouti (Afars and Issas). Somalia then (July 1977) used its Soviet arms to attempt to 'regain' the Somali-speaking Ogaden region of Ethiopia. The Soviet Union stopped arms supplies to Somalia, whereupon Somalia expelled its Soviet advisers and in early 1978 found itself fighting a losing war in the Ogaden against Ethiopian and some 16 000 Cuban troops directed by Soviet generals.[5] A return to the status quo — except for many thousands of refugees — was brought about with the help of the United States and Saudi Arabia. During the fighting, Iraq had assisted Somalia with planeloads of Soviet-supplied arms flown in Soviet-built transport aircraft. A West Somali Liberation Front in the south-eastern Ogaden continues to harass the Ethiopian forces, as do occasional forays by Somali regular forces.

But the Soviets were faced by even greater dilemmas than this in Ethiopia. First was that they found themselves in an embarrassing partnership with Israel which was also providing military advice in order if possible to keep the Eritrean coast out of Arab hands. Again, in strategic terms, Ethiopia would only adequately replace what the USSR had lost in Somalia if it offered assured access to the ports on the Eritrean coast, notably Assab and Massawa, with a secure hinterland, and if Ethiopia itself were politically stable. The country is by no means politically stable, even though Assab and Massawa are now under government control. The Soviet navy has obtained access to and is building a base in the Dahlak archipelago, off Eritrea. It has also upgraded the former British airstrip on the island of Socotra and has full use of the base at Aden. Right wing (Ethiopian Democratic Union) and various minority forces are a constant source of instability. The Eritrean Liberation movements, supported by virtually all the Arab states, except South Yemen (PDRY), have clung stubbornly to much of their territory and have largely repulsed Ethiopian assaults against them. Although the Soviets and the Cubans have tried to keep clear of this activity, their support of Mengistu and their brief* co-operation

---

* Israeli advisers were sent home as soon as their presence became public knowledge.

with Israel confused their attempts to win favour with the Arab world.

Shifting and complex though this all is it also represents a continuous, forceful and multi-directional Soviet attack on targets of opportunity in Africa. The Soviets have no monopoly on wisdom, influence or power in the region, but they keep trying, keep pressing for weaknesses, keep offering arms and ideology, although the ideology is far less in demand than the arms and the influence which arms give. Losses in one place are balanced by gains in another. It is a remarkably persistent programme of aggressive diplomacy on a wide front, based overwhelmingly on military factors.

Zimbabwe/Rhodesia

In recent years Soviet support of 'liberation' movements has been mainly concentrated in southern Africa. In Zimbabwe/Rhodesia prior to independence it provided arms and military advisers to the Zimbabwe African People's Union (ZAPU) led by Joshua Nkomo. The Soviet Union was suspicious of and lukewarm to the other main part of the divided Patriotic Front, the Zimbabwe African National Union (ZANU) led by Robert Mugabe, even though he declared himself to be a Marxist. The guerrilla actions of these two groups supported by neighbouring black states, plus pressure by the Western powers on South Africa which was white Rhodesia's main economic support, eventually forced the Smith government to concede some power to the black leader, Bishop Abel Muzorewa, and then to agree to the 1979 Lancaster House arrangement which provided for general elections. Both South Africa, which had backed Muzorewa, and the Soviet Union, which had backed ZAPU, misjudged the electorate which returned Mugabe by a sizable majority. There is thus government by a black nationalist majority but Mugabe will need all his evident political skills to contain the situation. He has a divided black electorate whose members could not even co-operate in the rebellion against white authority. Civil war was a way of life for many of them for years. Can they adjust to peace? The economy still depends on the goodwill of South Africa and on the capacity of blacks to replace departing whites in almost every area of economic activity. Mugabe will be under continuing pressure from other black African states and from the Soviet bloc to support the campaign against South Africa and there are already reports that Mugabe's restive coalition partner, ZAPU, is again reaching out for Soviet bloc arms.

The Soviet Union, Cuba, Hungary, Bulgaria and China have all given aid to Mozambique, and to its 'Marxist' President Machel, yet the country is heavily dependent economically on South Africa (from the returned earnings of expatriate mine labourers) and on South Africa's transport technology, and although Mozambique provided a refuge for Zimbabwe (ZANU) guerrillas it was never able to protect them against Rhodesian reprisals nor to crush its own rebel resistance movement. The FRELIMO government is clearly not in the Soviet pocket.

As we have seen, it is simplistic to speak of a 'belt of black communist states' across Africa. Soviet influence is diffused and — in varying degrees — resisted.

South Africa

The last fortress, or *laager*, of white supremacy on the African continent is in South Africa and its dependency South-West Africa[6] or Namibia. This is the remaining target for black liberation movements armed by the Soviet bloc. Operating against Namibia is the South-West African People's Liberation Organisation (SWAPO) which is based mainly in Angola and which by UN resolution is formally the only authentic representative of the Namibian people. Yet even UN resolutions cannot convert rhetoric into reality. Under external pressure the South African government has allowed a measure of self-government and considerable relaxation of racial segregation in Namibia, but manoeuvring between the UN, a group of five Western powers, South Africa and SWAPO has not yet produced the basis for an independent constitution. The Western powers would be better placed and more inclined to force South Africa in this direction if Namibia were not so richly endowed with uranium. It also encloses the South African port of Walvis Bay. The Caprivi Strip of Namibia separates Zambia and Angola from Botswana, and is strongly defended by South Africa.

The sense which most white South Africans have of being under siege relates to the restive local black majority,[7] the communist-assisted liberation movements operating into and in South Africa, the hostility of neighbouring black states, the general international condemnation of apartheid, and their own fear of Soviet military power.

Only limited and, to African eyes, largely superficial changes have been introduced to meet the demands of the non-white population, so that there is an unrelenting if uneven increase in the pressures building up within the society. Effective armed forces, police and intelligence services are largely able to cope with most guerrilla activity and could probably defeat any African forces sent against them. The states such as Zambia which have some sophisticated Soviet equipment (MiG-21s) do not have the industrial and military basis for mounting major operations. It is possible that Cubans could be used, but they would find the South African army — as they found it in Angola — a much tougher proposition than any other forces so far encountered. One cannot see Cubans embarking enthusiastically on such a venture; much less can one envisage the USSR becoming embroiled in a land war in Africa.

Why should the Soviet Union want to overthrow the South African government? South Africans reply, 'To acquire our minerals and to dominate the Cape route between the Indian Ocean and Europe'. As indicated above, for almost all the main minerals of which southern Africa is the West's principal supplier, the Soviet Union is the largest alternative source. Although obvious to an outsider, it is hard for South Africans to credit that all domestic unrest may not be communist-inspired, especially as Moscow has provided arms and funds to the banned African National Congress, some of whose leaders are members of the banned South African Communist Party. (Another black African movement, the Pan African Congress, has been supported by China.) Except by nuclear war, or a massive conventional assault, the Soviet Union is incapable of invading and overwhelming South Africa and even if it succeeded it would have no support structure for effectively administering the country. The most it could hope for would be a black African government sympathetic to Moscow. Certainly if the Soviet Union had access to the naval and air base facilities in South Africa it would be strategically well placed to carry out surveillance in the south Atlantic and western Indian Oceans, but there are almost 2 500 kilometres between Cape Point and the ice, and to sink ships is an act of war.

For reasons of both internal and external security, South Africa has long hoped to be part of the Western alliance defence system, but the West has been embarrassed by the notion, has been strongly critical of apartheid and has not needed South Africa in its strategic planning. There is considerable Western investment in South Africa, which is a major producer of gold and diamonds and which controls Namibia's uranium, but so long as South Africa can defend itself there is no reason why Europe or the US should do so. In the event of an East-West conventional war, South Africa is firmly placed in the West and could only be disadvantaged if it did not place its facilities at the West's disposal.

South Africa has taken steps towards producing nuclear weapons, and has carefully spread the impression that it could have them quite quickly. In October 1979 there were unconfirmed reports of a nuclear explosion at sea off the South African coast. While possession of nuclear weapons might offer some satisfaction to the white

South Africans, it is hard to see how such weapons could be used in South Africa's defence[8] in any of the situations that appear at all likely to threaten it. The most likely situation is growing urban violence, against which nuclear weapons of course are useless as, in the long run, are even the most efficient police and soldiery unless accompanied by the skilful and enlightened policies no South African government has yet displayed.

One must assume that it is not too late for that to occur. The later it occurs, the more difficult and more violent will be the transition to a multi-racial society and the more unstable will that society be. In any such transition the Western powers are unlikely to play a part, whereas the Soviet bloc will presumably fuel the flames, seeking opportunities from any chaos it may help to create.

The Indian Ocean

The Indian Ocean is an area of strategic competition first because it is there; second because in the north-western corner is located the principal world source of surplus oil; and third because it includes major highways of international commerce and the essential maritime route between the eastern and western parts of the Soviet Union.[9] For the first 60 years of this century Britain was the dominant seapower in the region, by its ubiquity* rather than by its strength, with France as a close second. But in the past 20 years the whole strategic situation has changed as most of the littoral states emerged from colonial status into nationhood, Britain retired to Europe, the Soviet Union developed a global military outreach, oil became a scarce and expensive commodity, and the increased range of SLBMs made the Indian Ocean a possible area from which to attack the Soviet Union.

The visit by a small squadron from the Soviet Pacific fleet to India and a number of other Indian Ocean ports in early 1968 marked the beginning of a Soviet naval presence that now has an air of permanence and averages 25–30 ships of which about half are combatants. The reasons for this development, in an area in which the Soviet Union has no territory, can only be guessed at, but presumably include the following:

1 The need to protect Soviet shipping between the USSR's two extremities;

---

* And, up to 1947, by the availability of Indian military forces.

2 The need to constrain and in war if possible prevent American SSBNs from operating in the Ocean against the Soviet Union;
3 The desire to project military power and political and economic influence in a region much of which has become a major-power vacuum;
4 The desire to protect and further Soviet interests in the Gulf-Arab oil producing areas, and 'spike the guns' of hostile powers; or, alternatively, the desire to be able to threaten Western access to Middle East oil;
5 The desire to obtain the oceanographic and hydrographic information necessary for the most efficient use of naval power. Although not strictly a defence matter, the Soviet Union also seeks to ascertain the maritime (including sea-bed) resources of the region, with the prospect of exploiting them in due course. It has maintained a sizable research programme in the ocean for more than twenty years.

Although the United States has long been the largest external trader into the Indian Ocean, until the mid-70s it kept only two or three naval ships in the area, based on the Gulf, with occasional visits by larger forces in times of tension (such as the 1971 India-Pakistan war). A decade earlier Britain had separated the Chagos Archipelago in the centre of the ocean from the colony of Mauritius, prior to moving the latter to independence, and made the island of Diego Garcia available for an American communications facility and naval outpost. A US radio facility capable of communicating with submerged submaries was built at North West Cape in Western Australia. In the 1970s, several situations prompted the United States administration to upgrade the American presence in the region over considerable objections from the US Congress. The first was the 1973 Arab-Israel war when oil embargo threats produced an almost unanimous unwillingness by the European NATO partners to facilitate American resupply of Israeli forces. This made the United States look more closely at resupply across the Pacific and Indian Oceans, the 'west-about' route, and at the whole problem of securing continued access to Gulf oil. The second was Soviet acquisition of a base in Somalia (Berbera) and its development of anti-submarine and then fixed-wing aircraft carriers (with a primarily anti-submarine role). Then came the Soviet-Cuban operations in Angola which marked a new phase of the deployment of Soviet bloc power. There was also Soviet cultivation of North Yemen, then of South (the People's Democratic Republic of) Yemen, with access to the former British bases at Aden and the use of Socotra. (When the Soviet Union replaced the United States in 1977–78 as the main supporting power of the regime in Ethiopia, the role of the US communications facility as Asmara was transferred to Diego Garcia.) Then came the fall of the Shah of Iran and the ejection of American personnel and influence, followed by the Soviet invasion of Afghanistan. The Soviet Union appeared to be welding a clamp around the oil producing region, and establishing the equivalent of the British coaling stations, the new links of an expanding empire. Britain had evacuated its bases at Aden, Singapore, and Gan (in the Maldives). 'Where you move out we move in', a Soviet official told a British friend of this writer, and although not as simple as that there is too much truth in it for comfort. The American response to the latest developments has been to expand the Diego Garcia facilities, deploy much larger naval forces in the Indian Ocean and the Gulf, have a 'Rapid Deployment Force' available for military operations in the region, and obtain limited access to facilities in Kenya, Egypt, Somalia and Oman. The United States would like more secure and more sophisticated base facilities outside but not too far from the Gulf region.

France also retains some naval units in the ocean, based on the French territory of Réunion in the south and on the dependency of Djibouti on the Red Sea — both strategically well placed for the southern trade routes and for the oil-producing area, and presumably a plus in the Western strategic assets.

India, the largest nation and military power in the whole region, is essentially a local power. It is not an object of strategic competition between East and West. India's greatest fear is an attack from China, against which only the Soviet Union offers the requisite degree of protection. The 1971 treaty with the Soviet Union insured India against a Chinese reaction when India invaded East Pakistan. After a brief experiment in a more even-handed 'non-alignment' under the Janata government (1976–9), India has returned to a greater degree of dependence than ever on Soviet arms, with a $1.6 billion deal in mid-1980. Although determined to be as sovereign as possible, India cannot fail at some time to pay a price for this dependence. At the same time, India's limited nuclear weapons programme has presumably been the main factor in Pakistan's decision to move towards a nuclear option, and this threatens an escalation on the sub-continent that neither country can afford with the possibility of an exchange neither could 'win'.

It is impossible to draw up an accurate balance sheet for Africa and the Indian Ocean as between Eastern and Western strategic interests, but one can say categorically that in the past decade the Soviet Union has extended its influence dramatically over a wide area. The picture is still complicated and fluid with many uncertainties. The USSR is the latest pretender to hegemonial power, and there is no other in Africa; it presses wherever it can in an area into which, until the invasion of Afghanistan, it had penetrated widely and in a few places deeply. The most important effect of the Afghanistan war may well turn out to be the stimulus it gave to the United States to renew its concern for deterring Soviet expansion at the margins of superpower confrontation, but it is difficult to see where in Africa that concern may be effectively manifested.

Eastern Asia and the Pacific

Whereas in Europe there is a relatively uncomplicated confrontation between two alliances, in Eastern Asia there is a triangular great power relationship that involves China, and an American alliance system that includes three potentially complicating elements: Japan as a willing client but somewhat reluctant ally; the Republic of (South) Korea which makes the United States a hostage to peninsular animosities and ambitions; the Republic of China (Taiwan) still dependent on American arms but continuingly if decreasingly (one may hope) a thorn in the side of Chinese-American rapprochement. Again, despite rumblings and dissonances within the two confronting European treaty partnerships, they remain substantially intact and monolithic, and the balance is shifting but singular and reasonably secure. In Eastern Asia there has been one disturbance after another, such as the successful Chinese revolution in 1949, the Korean War in 1950, the communist insurgencies in Southeast Asia from 1948 onwards, the breakdown of the Sino-Soviet agreement in 1959, the Sino-Indian border war of 1962, the Vietnam wars, Indonesia's bid for regional hegemony under Sukarno, and in the 1970s China's rapprochement with Japan and the United States and its war with Vietnam. Each of these represented and produced a change in the structure of power.

The Korean War appeared as evidence to the West that the communist power they sought to contain in Europe would embark on military adventures whenever opportunity offered. Coming on top of the Berlin blockade and the consolidation of Soviet power in Eastern Europe, it gave added impetus to Western military cooperation. But since the Korean War and the Indo-China settlement at Geneva in July 1954, the East Asian balance has been maintained or adjusted largely independent of events in other parts of the world. This is because China has been essentially a continental power, despite mild diplomatic forays into Africa, the Middle East and Europe; Japan has been busy rebuilding its economic strength; and the United States has had the capacity until very recently to manage concurrent commitments in several parts of the world and entertain simultaneous confrontations towards China and the Soviet Union.

This all began to change in the 1970s. The Nixon-Kissinger axis that inherited the failed enterprise in Vietnam marked for the US a turning away from ideology as the mainspring of foreign policy and from a universal anti-communist crusade as its vehicle. Peking and Washington reached out for at least the formality of contact in the context of growing Soviet power in Asia, while Moscow and Washington engaged in detente — a process of accommodation that lasted so long as its different objectives remained obscure. The great traumas of Vietnam which made detente welcome in Washington also produced the American weaknesses which the USSR was able to exploit through its forward policy in Africa (Angola, Ethiopia), south-west Asia (Afghanistan, South Yemen), south Asia (the treaty with India that reassured the latter as it administered the *coup de grace* to East Pakistan) and Southeast Asia (Vietnam). With the fall of the Shah and the Soviet invasion of Afghanistan, the world realised what American officials had long understood: that the United States could only engage in conventional war in south-west Asia (to protect oil supplies) or in Europe (perhaps to help Yugoslavia) by depleting its forces in Asia — a concept which became known in 1979, with transparent euphemism, as the 'swing strategy'. This decline in American capacity has coincided with greater Soviet self-confidence, military strength and assertiveness, based on or accompanied by the achievement of strategic parity with the US.

Sino-Soviet confrontation

As of late 1980, the Soviet Union deployed in its eastern (Asian) zone some 38 motorised rifle divisions plus 6 tank divisions facing China, 2 divisions in Sakhalin, 1 at Petropavlovsk, up to 2 divisions in the Kurils including the former Japanese territories, and 3 in Mongolia — a total of about 650 000 troops. There are substantial air units, including some *Backfire* bombers, and several hundred ICBMs and IRBMs including mobile SS-20s. The Pacific fleet includes 30 ballistic missile submarines, 23 cruise missile submarines and 57 attack submarines, 79 surface combat ships, one ASW aircraft carrier, 73 amphibious ships, and some 700 smaller ships and patrol craft operating out of five main naval bases and other ports.[10]

Facing the Soviets, the Chinese are reported to deploy 72 divisions of about 1 260 000 men. The Chinese are far less well equipped than the Soviets; they have few, if any, modern anti-tank missiles, few armoured personnel carriers, and only a third of the number of tanks the USSR has deployed. China's air defence system is much less sophisticated than the Soviet Union's. Deployed against Soviet targets are about 50 MRBMs, 30 IRBMs, and perhaps 10 ICBMs, plus a few obsolescent bombers. There is no evidence that missile sites are 'hardened'.

Thus, although the Soviet Union with its nuclear weapons could undoubtedly destroy Chinese cities and indeed Chinese civilisation, it would be vulnerable to Chinese retaliation, unless it pre-emptively destroyed (as it probably could) all Chinese missile sites. And though in conventional terms it could penetrate deep into China, it does not at present have in the Soviet Far East the capacity to engage in sustained offensive operations against the People's Republic. It could 'walk in' but not 'walk out'.

The Sino-Soviet relationship lies at the heart of the East Asian strategic balance. Except briefly in the 1950s, it has never been a happy relationship, but in this last decade and more it has been (with rare ameliorations) increasingly acrimonious. The basis of this hostility is mutual fear. In the Soviet case, it is a fear ingrained by centuries of history reaching back to the Mongol invasion and compounded by the size of the Chinese population; fear exacerbated by guilt over the seizure of 'Chinese' territory over the past 120 years; fear underlain by racist or at least racialist sentiments, and accentuated by China's possession of nuclear missiles. The USSR claims to be troubled by the possibility of Chinese-inspired disaffection among border communities, although standards of living are higher on the Soviet side. It is concerned at the vulnerability of the Trans-Siberian Railway which is the main form of transport communications with the eastern area, and it is in the process of building a second segment, from 150 to 500 kilometres to the north (the Baikal-Amur Mainline Railway (BAM), from Taishet through Bratsk, Ust-Kut, Komsomolsk-na-Amure to Sovetskaya Gavan on the Pacific Coast). A long and enormously difficult project, it is expected to be complete in about 1985.

The Chinese resent past Soviet acquisitiveness and they are still angry at being left in the lurch of their technological backwardness in 1959. They fear the enormous military capacities of the Soviet Union, including its nuclear armoury against which China has little defence,[11] and its veiled or unveiled threats.

The mutual hostility has other dimensions of an ideological and political nature, over the purity of Marxist doctrine and the exercise of leadership in the communist world. Resentments have built on one another, action bringing inevitable reaction, the battle of words and gestures developing a momentum of its own and giving substance to suspicion. Although different in many ways from the East-West confrontation in Europe, the Sino-Soviet confrontation along their 10 000 kilometres of common border is no less fundamentally hostile and no more likely to be resolved by detente diplomacy. The Soviet Union cannot and will not provide the technology, capital and arms required to make China the secure, modern industrial state it aims optimistically to be by the year 2000 or soon after. Only the West (including Japan) can come near to doing so, and no Chinese government is now likely to jeopardise that possibility for an uncertain reconciliation with its truculent superpower neighbour.

Most Chinese arms are a generation or more behind those of the Soviet Union, and the Chinese know that the Soviet Union could successfully defeat any Chinese attack and could launch a massive conventional strike deep into China. But just as Napoleon and Hitler were defeated by the vastness of Russia, so is any invader ultimately defeated by the vastness of China, the size of its population, and the immensity of the task of administration. Despite their periodically ritualised animosities and occasional border incidents, both China and the USSR know that neither can gain from a war between them. China has no threat on the east but it does have two potentially hostile borders — against the Soviet Union and Vietnam. The Soviet Union occupies both extremities of the continent with a potential enemy at each. A war at one end must weaken its capacity to defend the other. The nightmare of Soviet planners is simultaneous conflict in Asia and Europe.

China + Japan + US = ?

The problems of defending the eastern part of the Soviet empire have been compounded in recent years by the new relationship between China on the one hand and the United States and Japan on the other. The Soviet Union had plenty of warning of this development from the 1971 Kissinger visit to Peking until the full normalisation of US-Chinese relations and the Sino-Japanese treaty of 1978. While the Soviet Union could not have prevented these developments, this was the time when a Moscow government with any finesse would have worked to improve relations with China, Japan, or both; but such is the power of dogma and of entrenched attitudes that it did neither, virtually forcing Japan into the treaty by public threats and by military moves in the northern islands of Japan occupied by the USSR since 1945 (see below).

China's attitudes towards the United States were a function both of the degree of American involvement in Vietnam,[12] and of its commitments to South Korea and Taiwan. President Nixon's 1972 visit to China became possible when American troops were out of Vietnam. With the final defeat of the South Vietnamese forces in

1975, and thus the total humiliation of American policy there, the Chinese government feared that the Soviet Union would take advantage of the American mood of retrenchment to launch its own more assertive policies in Asia. China also wanted to make use of Western technology to strengthen the country's individual capacity. It knew it could only do this by means of a diplomatic rapprochement with the United States, a rapprochement which was facilitated by Kissinger's Soviet-oriented sense of strategic realities and by the strong residual pro-Chinese (if anti-communist) sentiment in the United States. China reversed its policy on Japan, supported Japanese-American defence links, and condemned the Soviet Union for its pressure on Japan. The post-Mao government moved as fast as it could to create a new anti-Soviet alignment in eastern Asia, reaching out for Western capital, industry, technology, education and even tourists for currency. The objectives were security against the USSR, and 'modernisation' of the Chinese economy. The costs included ending the Sino-Soviet treaty of 1950 (which had been directed against Japan and the US, and was now largely a formality); bypassing most aspects of the question of Taiwan and allowing the United States to continue to provide Taiwan with arms; and making a major change in public dogma. These, and especially the last, would probably have been impossible for the post-Mao predominantly Shanghainese radical-left leadership symbolised by the 'Gang of Four', but were less difficult for their successors, the more conservative, pragmatic coalition of which Deng Xiaoping has been the dominant spirit and the deeply respected late Chou En-lai the necessary foundation-layer.

China's rapprochement with Japan meant less and involved less than that with the United States. Japan had signed a treaty with the Republic of [Nationalist] China after World War II, but it had not committed itself (as had the US) to the defence of Taiwan. Japan had distanced itself as much as it could from America's Vietnam policies. There had been no treaty of peace between the People's Republic and Japan but after a time this did not affect trade, investment, civil aviation, cultural exchanges or tourism, which built up considerably during the 1970s under a whole series of official and semi-official agreements. The Japanese did not particularly want or need a treaty with China, but China pressed for it and one (of Peace and Friendship) was finally signed in August 1978. The inducement to Japan was a more assured access to China's probably immense but still to be determined natural resources and to its glittering promise of new markets. The treaty would also defuse any residual Chinese hostility towards Japan. The incentives for China were to obtain greater access to Japan's technological capacity, and to align Japan psychologically with China against the Soviet Union. By forc-

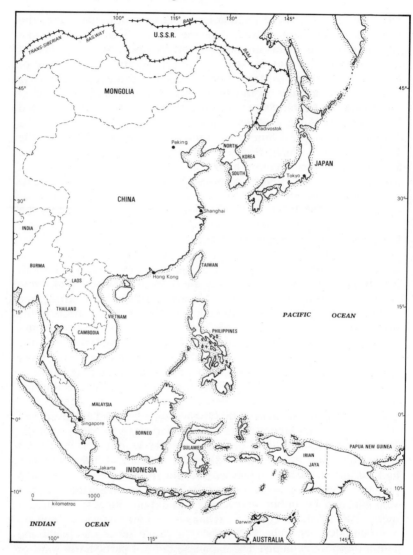

6 East Asia

ing the issue on the second point — insisting that the treaty include
a clause opposing efforts by any other country (i.e. the USSR) to
establish hegemony in the ASEAN Pacific region — China won a
temporary triumph which a Japanese disclaimer[13] did not alleviate
but which Japan knew the Soviet Union would see — or claim — as
gratuitously offensive.

Japan had two other inducements of dubious validity. Late in the negotiations the Chinese used blunt-instrument diplomacy over the Senkaku or Tiao-yu-t'ai islands north of Taiwan. These islands, uninhabited and apparently unclaimed by anyone else, were incorporated into Japan's Okinawa Prefecture in 1895. They were later claimed by communist China and by the Nationalist government in Taiwan. They were formally 'handed back' to Japan by the United States in 1972, and in recent years have been the subject of unconfirmed reports that they sat on large oil deposits. By a remarkable unity of mind, in April 1978 several hundred Chinese fishing boats circled the islands and unfurled banners declaring that the islands belonged to China.[14] After Japanese protests, the Chinese government apparently assured Tokyo that there would be no further protests of this kind and proposed that the question of sovereignty be deferred. As a show of ownership, Japan has recently erected a hydrographic station on one of the islands. The second inducement — if such it was — related to Korea which was Japanese territory from 1910 to 1945. Successive Japanese governments have long felt the security of Korea to be vital to the security of Japan.[15] Rumours circulated in Japan in 1978 that China had assured Japan that it would use its influence to restrain any aggressive inclinations of North Korea's President Kim Il Sung. These were apparently confirmed by Premier Hua Guofeng during his visit to Tokyo in June 1980.[16]

Japanese attitudes to China have never been as apprehensive as some Western analysts have expected them to be. Although Japanese are conscious of the iniquities they perpetrated in China during the 1931–45 period, they also have a disarming sense of common cultural derivation. They tend to feel, not always accurately, that they understand China and the Chinese, have much in common with them and, despite various disagreements, little to fear from them.[17] Japan's armed forces are small (they total about 240 000). Although this situation has begun to change, for a long time they lacked public or adequate legislative support,[18] and are still essentially defensive in their armament and doctrine. They are well-equipped but quite inadequate to defend the country against a major assault. China has never had, and does not look like having, such an assault capacity.

The industry and technology that have made Japan the third largest economy in the world are fed by imported raw materials. These make the economy vulnerable, especially to constraints on oil. The 1973 OPEC decisions caused a panic in Japan and political capitulation over the Arab-Israel question. Subsequent measures to reduce Japan's vulnerability to oil pressures, such as stockpiling, oil exploration, negotiating alternative oil supplies, and expansion of civil nuclear energy plants, have made only a modest impact on both government and private apprehensions.

Japan's anxieties

Yet such fears are small and selective compared with the permanent and pervasive Japanese anxieties about the Soviet Union. They go back well into the last century, since when (until 1945) Japan and Russia competed for power and territory in their joint region at the expense of each other [19] and of the Chinese and Koreans. In August 1945, with its last-minute entry into the war against Japan, the Soviet Union revenged itself for its defeat in the war of 1904–5 and acquired the whole of Sakhalin and the Kuril islands, including Etorofu and Kunashiri.

While the main current dispute between the two states relates to those last two islands plus the Habomais and Shikotan, these are counters in a much larger contest. The historic Soviet maritime problem of access to the open seas has been compounded in Asia by the ice reaching for much of the year well down in the sea of Okhotsk as well as by Japan's strategic dominance of the exits from that sea past Sakhalin, the Kurils, and Tsushima. This is one reason why the Soviet Union is unlikely ever to return any of the Kurils to Japan (although the Habomais and Shikotan make little strategic difference). A second and perhaps equally important reason is that any return of Soviet-controlled territory to Japan would be seen as establishing a precedent which China could use with respect to the far larger areas of once-Chinese land now part of the Soviet Union. China's continued public support for Japan's claim to the island emphasises the possibility.

But the main Soviet concern about Japan these past 30 years has been its use as a forward base for American power (part of the 7th Fleet and the 5th Air Force) which is a direct challenge or counter to Soviet power in the region. In recent years the Japanese government has contributed to the cost of upkeep of the US bases. The 1960 US-Japan Mutual Security Treaty, though including the standard flexible provision that in the event of armed attack each will 'act to meet the common danger in accordance with its constitutional provisions and processes', is widely assumed in Japan, the US and elsewhere to place an American military umbrella over Japan. It has allowed Japan consistently to spend less than 1%[20] of GNP on defence, and to concentrate on the development of its economy. Rarely, if ever, has a defeated enemy been so generously treated by the victor, so ably protected, so encouraged to become so formidable an economic competitor.

The Soviet-Japanese relationship has curious ambivalences, with Soviet diplomacy inclined to threats and Japan's to concessions, but with some hard ground in the middle. The Soviet Union would like Japanese capital and technology to help extract the vast natural resources of Siberia, and Japan would like access to those resources, especially oil, as well as other minerals and timber. During the late 1970s several agreements were negotiated to this end, but with decreasing enthusiasm from the Japanese side which saw itself as being used for Soviet economic and strategic advantage. Japan wanted the insurance of American participation, but this was not forthcoming. For centuries Japanese have fished in Russian waters and vice versa. To give themselves leverage, the Soviets toughened their stance, confiscated hundreds of Japanese boats and catches and imprisoned the crews, and have insisted on annual cliff-hanging negotiations. The Soviet Union 'punished' Japan's rapprochement with China by fortifying Etorofu, Kunashiri, the Habomais and Shikotan. As they do to Norway and indeed to Britain, Soviet aircraft annually fly hundreds of intimidating and intelligence-gathering sorties near the Japanese mainland; intelligence ships are anchored just off the territorial limits. In the Sea of Japan, the Japanese navy feels intimidated by Soviet vessels. Yet Japan in 1978 built on credit and towed to Vladivostok an 80 000-tonne dry dock suitable for servicing Soviet aircraft carriers. Japan has so far refused to be browbeaten into signing a treaty of good neighbourliness with the Soviet Union produced as a transparent counter-attraction to the Japan-China agreement. The reasons for the complex and ambivalent Japanese policies are comparatively simple. It has no alternative to living alongside two giant neighbours and has no intention of offending either unnecessarily. Further, as a Japanese professor once said to me, 'World War II taught Japan that to pursue economic ends by military means is a most uneconomical proposition'. Peace has her victories more profitable, if less renowned, than war.

A factor in Japanese calculations must be the shifting balance between the Soviet and the American forces in the north-east Asian region and the western Pacific generally. On a straight comparison of naval combat capacity, while it is impossible to equate types of ships, the Soviet navy (see p. 138) is now far more extensive — it has fewer carriers but more submarines and surface combat vessels. According to the US Joint Chiefs of Staff, 2 US carriers and about 20 cruisers are normally deployed in the western Pacific, plus 2 amphibious readiness groups with Marine elements embarked, one operating out of California and one out of Japan (Okinawa and Honshu). Strategic bombers and ballistic missile submarines operate from Guam. Tactical fighter squadrons, tactical airlift squadrons and naval patrol aircraft operate from Guam, Japan (including Okinawa), Korea and the Philippines where the United States has an air base at Clark Field near Manila and a naval base at Subic Bay.[21] An infantry division is based at Honolulu. Another, based in the Republic of Korea, has been partly withdrawn; total withdrawal has been delayed by Korean and presumably by Japanese and other pressures and it is now unlikely to be completed for some years. According to the IISS's publication, *The Military Balance 1980–81*, the US 3rd Fleet, based in California and Alaska, has 4 carriers and 67 surface combatants. Significant elements of the 3rd and 7th Fleets were detached during 1980 to the Indian Ocean and the Gulf.

Pacific naval balance

In any calculation of the western Pacific naval balance, the Western forces must include those of Japan which has 14 submarines, 33 destroyers, 15 frigates, with 3 more submarines, 6 destroyers and 2 frigates on order; Western forces also include Australia's, with its 6 submarines, an aircraft carrier, 4 destroyers and 6 frigates.

Senior American officers have expressed fears that the United States could not assure safe passage of merchant shipping west of Honolulu. In fact, such is Soviet submarine capacity that American shipping east of Honolulu would also be vulnerable, despite the existence in the eastern Pacific of the US 3rd Fleet. But it is not only comparative military capacity that has troubled Japanese, it is also comparative will, and until very recently the American mood in Asia has been one of retrenchment under an expanded form of the 'Nixon doctrine' of 1969–70 whereby Asian partners of the US were expected to be more self-reliant, i.e. less dependent on American power.

For much of the 1970s, and increasingly, the United States has been pressing Japan to spend more on defence, and thanks to Soviet activities in the Sea of Japan and surrounding airspace, and to the Afghanistan war, rather than to American exhortation, the 1980–81 Japanese budget made such a provision, although defence spending is still within the figure of 1% of GNP. The US has also pressed for greater co-ordination of defence effort and planning which the Japanese, for a time, strongly though not totally resisted. There is a Security Consultative Committee arising from the Mutual Security Treaty. In July 1976 this Committee set up a sub-committee for Defence Co-operation which two and a half years later recommended 'Guidelines for Japan-United States Defence Co-operation'.[22] Again, the Soviet local activities and the invasion of Afghanistan have given this co-operation a degree of immediacy not previously acknowledged by Tokyo.

The Japan-US relationship is based on mutual advantage, not least in trade since each is the largest overseas market of the other. The US strategic position in the western Pacific depends substantially on its access to American bases in Japan[23] and especially to Yokosuka, which has the largest dry dock west of the continental United States. American protection offers strategic and economic advantages to Japan but in political terms it is a mixed blessing, a public demonstration of dependence. Japanese foreign policy is a continuing process of trying to reduce the public appearance of dependence while maintaining the private fact whereas the United States objective is to seek to increase Japan's self-reliance and its contribution to the security of the region but not to the point where it would run an independent foreign policy and deny facilities to the Americans. The return of a clear conservative majority in the Japanese elections of July 1980, within a more tense international climate, lent solidity to the alliance. One must assume that in the long term Japan, with a population of 108 million and the world's third largest GNP, will want to stand more squarely and demonstrably on its own feet, exerting influences and taking initiatives. Even now there are Japanese who believe that in a crisis the United States, as it did in Vietnam and Taiwan, would renege on its commitments to Japan, although the whole defence policy is built on the assumption that it will not.

Immediately following the signing of the Sino-Japanese treaty, the then Foreign Minister Sonoda declared that Japan would not co-operate in the modernisation of China's armed forces. Yet if Japan can sell a dockyard to the Soviet Union, and if the British can build a Rolls Royce factory in China and (as seems likely) sell her military aircraft, then what may not Japan and the United States (with a Most Favoured Nation trading clause) sell her in the way of defence or defence-related equipment? In matters commercial Japan, like the Oscar Wilde character, can resist everything except temptation.

American reactions to the revolution in Iran and to the taking of American hostages shook the US-Japan relationship but when the Soviet Union invaded Afghanistan the Japanese proved to be America's most forthcoming ally.[24] Although Japan might not quite see it this way, the United States now regards Japan as far more comfortable with an active political role in international affairs, as ready to identify itself as a full member of a wider Western alliance, and as prepared occasionally to set international political considerations ahead of commercial gain. Japan would put it differently: on the basis of its economic strength it is actively seeking a political role in international affairs, within a Western 'division of labour', but not a military role except in self-defence, and would like its

Western partners to see Japanese reluctance to rearm as an asset to be exploited rather than as an obstacle to be overcome.

Within the quadrilateral constellation marked by the USSR, China, Japan and the US, there are several lesser but influential stars: the two Koreas, Taiwan, Vietnam, Thailand the Philippines, as well as the Association of Southeast Asian Nations (ASEAN) as a group. All are relevant to the strategic balance.

The two Koreas

The Democratic Republic of (North) Korea, (DPRK) which, in June 1950 under its present leader Kim Il Sung, launched the attack on the South, repeatedly declares and periodically gives evidence that it would like to try again. Its action on the first occasion was apparently approved by Stalin and Mao, was armed by the USSR, and was saved by China from defeat at the hands of United Nations (mostly US) and Republic of Korea forces. The situation today is different. The DPRK is heavily in debt to both the USSR and China and relies on the Soviet Union for its more sophisticated military equipment but it has greater political and cultural affinities with China. These affinities are being strained by China's pragmatic opening to the West. The armed forces of North and South Korea are roughly equal in size, with the North having a preponderance in aircraft and tanks. South Korea still has a tripwire for US involvement in the form of part of an American division. So long as the tripwire remains it would make no sense for the North Koreans to restart a conflagration which they could not control and could have no hope of winning. Nor is China likely, with its present attitudes and objectives, to encourage a war between North Korea and the US. The United States also has naval and air forces based on South Korea which are of real military significance. There is a Unified Command which puts an American general in charge of all allied forces in Korea. Even if the US division were withdrawn — as the Carter administration wanted to do but found it could not — the residual American involvement would be considerable and the Republic of Korea forces are also formidable. There is no guarantee that North Korea's President Kim or his successor might not try to fulfil his long-standing promise to unify the country by force, hoping to drag his powerful allies in behind him, and to acquire eternal glory in the process. It would not be logical. It could not, in present circumstances, be expected to succeed.

South Korea is formally an ally of the United States, but the Republic of China (Taiwan) is no longer an ally, the security treaty having been allowed to lapse. The US continues to supply arms of a defensive nature. The attitude of the People's Republic to Taiwan is far more relaxed than it used to be. There is no bombing of Quemoy or Matsu. There is significant trade through Hong Kong but apparently also bilaterally. It would be surprising if there were not secret political contacts. There is no 7th Fleet in the Strait. Apart from questions of pride or acquisitiveness, Taiwan is no threat and does not stand in China's way, strategically, politically, or economically.

Taiwan

After 30 years of scenarios of war, — the threats and counter-threats, the millions of words spoken in acrimony from extreme positions on every side, the overblown ambitions of Taipei, the Republic of China is no longer either a potential great power or a pawn between the great powers. Its remarkable economic progress depends on remaining at peace and continuing to receive American and Japanese capital and technology. It would re-enter the strategic equation if it became a host to Soviet power or if it developed nuclear weapons. In both cases it would incur the anger of the People's Republic and the United States and almost certainly military retribution by the former. Short of giving such provocation, there is no reason why Taiwan should not continue as an independent, increasingly industrialised state off the coast of China with which it could develop mutually advantageous trading, investment and cultural relations.

Southeast Asia

Southeast Asia is a long way from the Soviet Union but the Soviet position there, and especially in Vietnam, arises from two perceived strategic requirements and two political opportunities. The first requirement is to be in a position to prevent closure to Soviet shipping of the straits through the Malay archipelago. The second is to contain China on the south, and to be able to bring pressure there as a counter to Chinese activities on their common border in the north and west. The first opportunity was provided by the Vietnam war and North Vietnam's need of communist bloc military and economic assistance, especially in the form of sophisticated defence against American air attack. The second opportunity was provided by the desire of the Socialist Republic of Vietnam (i.e. the state comprising North and South Vietnam after the North's final victory in 1975) to establish, in the face of Chinese opposition, hegemony over Laos and Kampuchea (Cambodia).

As early as June 1969, in response to the first significant publicised border clash between China and the Soviet Union, Mr Brezhnev began to promote the notion of a 'system of collective security in Asia', which the Soviet government has re-promoted from time to time. Never given, at least in public, any firm substance or defined shape, the notion brought little response from the states to which it was addressed, although India (in 1971) signed a bilateral treaty as an insurance against Chinese support of Pakistan during the Bangladesh war. Whatever the Soviet Union may have had in mind for the non-communist states of the region, the proposal had several drawbacks. It envisaged substituting Soviet protection for either American protection or for non-alignment. In return it seemed to offer nothing except a commitment to Soviet objectives. Further, in an area where China was the local great power and where there were 15–20 million 'overseas' Chinese, it was patently aimed at containing China, which would inevitably be offended. The one country where the idea of protection against China had immediate and lasting attraction was Vietnam.

Although one may believe that American or Western diplomacy towards North Vietnam and the SRV could have been more sophisticated and effectual, the US did not 'drive Vietnam into the arms of the Russians' in 1975 — they were there already, even if none too comfortably, and to a degree had been for 20 years. It was entirely clear to the Vietnamese government that only the Soviet Union had both the will and the capacity to be what Vietnamese for centuries had needed — a protector against China. Only the Soviet Union was prepared to give massive help to Vietnam's severely depleted economy. Only the Soviet Union would, in such circumstances, give the necessary help in weapons, oil and food to enable Vietnam to embark on the subjugation of Kampuchea (Laos was already effectively under Vietnamese control). In mid-1978, the SRV became a full member of CMEA, and in November it signed a Treaty of Friendship and Co-operation with the Soviet Union, the two sides undertaking to consult immediately in the event of an attack or threatened attack on either, and to take 'appropriate and effective measure' to safeguard their peace and security. The treaty went further than others between the Soviet Union and non-European states, with specifically intra-bloc declarations such as on co-ordinating economic plans.

Whatever the reasons for the initial Kampuchean-Vietnamese border clashes, Vietnam's invasion and occupation of Kampuchea changed the regional strategic balance. It aroused — as it continues to arouse — the apprehension of the non-communist states in the area, apprehension compounded by the forced or encouraged expulsion of more than a million (mainly racially Chinese)

Vietnamese, many of whom perished at sea, as well as several hundred thousand Laotians and Kampucheans. It brought China into a new and more sympathetic relationship with Thailand. It drew the Chinese response in January 1979, after a series of border incidents, of a brief and limited-objective invasion of Vietnam in an attempt to 'teach Vietnam a lesson'. The lesson intended was presumably that Vietnam should not attempt hegemony over Kampuchea, should not rely on Soviet protection, and should defer to Chinese policy objectives. The lessons learned by Vietnam were that it could fight a limited war with China and simultaneously occupy Kampuchea; that it would need Soviet help to defend itself against an all-out Chinese attack, and as a matter of not unreasonable faith that help would, if tardily, be forthcoming. Advanced Soviet surface-to-air missiles were established along the Vietnam-China border and large quantities of Soviet arms and equipment were shipped to Vietnam. Thus if any 'driving' of Vietnam was done, it was done by the Chinese. Vietnam suffered relatively far more than China from the war. Presumably it learned that China was not going to acquiesce in Vietnamese designs for regional hegemony. China no doubt learned a lot about weaknesses within the PLA and about the toughness of the Vietnamese forces which, in the event of any subsequent 'lesson', will be better equipped and more numerous. Vietnam now keeps some 40% of its ground forces as a defence against China, which prevents their deployment elsewhere.

The Soviet Union took advantage of the opportunities which the China-Vietnam war provided. Before this, the Vietnamese had been reluctant to allow the Soviets too public a representation or too obvious a military presence in Vietnam. Subsequently the Soviet Union installed a communications and radio-intercept station in Vietnam. Soviet warships, including submarines, make increasing use of the former American base at Cam Ranh Bay, and Soviet aircraft operating out of Da Nang are able to carry out surveillance operations over and beyond Southeast Asia and the South China Sea. Although still relatively modest in size, the Soviet presence in Vietnam has given a totally new dimension to the strategic equation in the area between India, Australia and the Philippines. No non-communist government in the region has welcomed this development and when the Soviet Union in September 1979 sought permission for some warships to visit ports in Thailand, Malaysia, the Philippines and Indonesia, it was rebuffed. It will no doubt try again.

Those four states, plus Singapore, constitute ASEAN, an initially economic but increasingly political and strategic partnership, supported de facto by the limited Five-Power defence arrangements between Malaysia, Singapore, Britain, Australia and New Zealand. The interests of the ASEAN states are diverse but fear of a Soviet-backed Vietnam has been a unifying force. Both Soviet and Vietnamese disclaimers of hostile intent towards Vietnam's neighbours have not assuaged those fears in the light of the Vietnamese army of occupation in Kampuchea, the Vietnamese-Thai clashes on the Thai-Kampuchean border, the increasing Soviet presence in the region, and the invasion of Afghanistan. On the other hand, all ASEAN members have sizable Chinese populations and a historic fear of Chinese hegemony. Some, such as Indonesia, are more inclined to see Vietnam as a buffer against China, than China as a buffer against Vietnam.

It would make no sense for Vietnam or for the Soviet Union if the former launched a war against Thailand. It would be costly for an already exhausted economy, would alarm the whole region, and would engage the United States. But Thailand, still under partial American protection through the otherwise defunct Southeast Asian Collective Defence Treaty (known by its organisation, SEA-TO), is caught between Soviet-Vietnamese pressures on the one hand and Chinese on the other. China continues to supply through Thailand the rump Pol Pot forces in Kampuchea. The border tensions, causing flutters of apprehension throughout the area, will continue so long as Vietnam is able to subdue most, but not the whole, of Kampuchea. In this situation, China has become for Thailand a welcome support as well as a cause of the danger for which the support is needed.

In July 1980 the London *Times* reported that China's Chairman Hua Guofeng was trying to build an informal alliance between China, the United States, Japan, Australia and Thailand (or ASEAN), perhaps in the shape of two 'triangles'.[25] Since 1978 Soviet press and radio have been referring to China's rapprochement with Japan and the US as having the nature of an alliance. If an alliance is a relationship where there is a declared commitment to and reasonable expectation of military action by the partners on behalf of any one of them who needs it, then the US-Japan treaty and the ANZUS treaty are alliances; but the US-China-Japan relationship is not an alliance and there are formidable obstacles to making it one.

The first obstacle is China itself; it wants all the psychological, material and military help it can get against the Soviet Union but it is not likely to offer military help to other powers (except perhaps Thailand) nor is it likely to conclude a formal military treaty with either Japan or the United States because of ideological differences. Japan is committed to the American partnership for the foreseeable future. It has semantically moved from a policy of 'equidistance' from China and the USSR to what was called an 'omni-directional' policy, i.e. looking with inscrutable amiability in all directions, and it would run against all Japanese instincts to ally with either China or the USSR against the other. One cannot conceive of the US Senate concluding a treaty that would oblige the United States to fight to defend China against the USSR. Nor would Japan agree to a treaty, bound as it is by the Constitution, nor would it welcome a situation under which it could be involved against the USSR by its security treaty with the United States.

But if a formal alliance is out of the question, degrees of co-operation in foreign policy, on economic matters and on military procurement are not, and they would seem likely to bind the three states into a general association which will appear increasingly in Moscow as having the character of — virtually *being* — an alliance. Thus the tendency in Asia, despite its more diverse structure, is towards the creation of the kind of dual confrontation that exists in Europe.

The strength of the Western part of that confrontation will remain indefinitely the United States, with its own bases on the West Coast, in Hawaii, and in its Pacific territories, and more precariously, in leased bases in Japan and the Philippines. Sites for US communications facilities and access to local bases are also provided by Australia. Japan and Australia (as well as New Zealand) appear stable partners, but it would be rash to assume that the bases in the Philippines will be perpetually available. Successive Filipino governments have charged increasing financial and political rents. There are many of the elements of a revolutionary situation in the country, even though it seems most likely that President Marcos will be succeeded by someone very like him.

In the south-west Pacific, Australia and New Zealand, which are backed by the ANZUS Treaty, offer a basis for stability among the island states as well as a source of civil and military aid. Japan and the Soviet Union have pressed for and obtained access to fishing within local 'economic zones'. There is little positive reason for the Soviet Union to seek more than this, yet the state of mind which has Soviet bloc forces and advisers scattered over so much of Africa will not necessarily abstain from considering Oceania in a similar light. It is not irrelevant that the Soviet Union, living about as far from the Antarctic continent as it is possible to be, has the majority of research stations there. Although demilitarised under the 1959 Antarctic Treaty, with all territorial claims held in abeyance, new processes of mineral extraction through thick ice will one day make Antarctica an area of competitive exploitation. It is essential, before that happens, for international institutions to draw up rules which make Antarctic resources part of the 'common heritage of mankind' for allocation according to human needs rather than brute strength.

Central and South America

For understandable if not always well-motivated reasons, the United States' attitudes to Central and South America have been almost exactly the opposite of her attitudes to Africa. When in December 1823 President James Monroe enunciated the doctrine which has since borne his name that there must be no further European colonisation in the Americas and no external intervention in the governments of the Western hemisphere, he was concerned primarily with Russian moves in Alaska and the possibility of Spain's attempting to regain control of rebellious colonies. But the Monroe Doctrine was not simply one of trying to keep Europe out of Latin America; it reflected, and was intended to reinforce, the notion that the United States had what we would now call hegemonial rights over all the double continent south of the Canadian border, that this region was a US 'sphere of influence' and of economic activity.

The Monroe Doctrine was never wholly enforceable and to the extent during the nineteenth century that it was enforced, it depended primarily on the power of the British navy. In this century the American government, armed forces and financial interests managed to operate the Doctrine adequately on their own, but not without considerable resentment and sometimes reprisals by Latin American governments. During World War II and subsequently, the US ostensibly managed its hemisphere policy through the Organisation of American States (OAS) and the Pan-American movement, but it was frequently unable to resist using the power it had to influence both foreign and domestic policies, especially against the rise of left-wing movements or administrations. In countries where right-wing civil or military dictatorship was endemic, where so much of the economy was owned by a tiny elite or by foreigners, and where for generations there have been great gaps between the rich and the poor, perhaps the only point of surprise is that left-wing populist movements have been so few and, for the most part, so ineffectual. There are many reasons for this. One is the limited extent of Soviet involvement, even though this began to change after World War II. Another is the Treaty of Rio, signed in September 1947, which provided for collective measures including the use of force in the event of threat to or attack upon any of the members, i.e. a quasi-legal cover was given for the United States to intervene to protect its interests against the direct or indirect actions of a foreign power, viz. the Soviet Union. This it did in Guatemala in 1954, where the National Democratic Front government led by Jacobo Arbenz included communists in important ministerial posts. Arbenz made the tactical errors of expropriating land owned by the United Fruit Company and other American concerns and of buying arms from

Czechoslovakia. The American CIA engineered an invasion by anti-communist Guatemalan exiles from neighbouring states and with a push from the Guatemalan army the Arbenz government fell.

There were many other expressions of left-wing political activity. In 1956 the left in Chile came together in the Socialist Party and then in the Popular Action Front (FRAP) under Salvador Allende, with strong communist elements. It eventually won office as the Popular Unity (UP) in 1970.

The Cuban revolution of 1958–9, while radical in nature and with communist participation, was not initially Soviet-oriented although it was soon to have strong anti-American overtones. Worsened relations with the US brought a series of retaliations and counter-retaliations, of which Mr Khrushchev took shrewd advantage, buying sugar and providing arms. By the end of 1960 Cuba was firmly in the Soviet camp where it still remains although it has not been a simple echo of Soviet foreign policy. The disastrous Bay of Pigs invasion by US-backed Cuban exiles could only have confirmed President Castro's anti-Americanism, but the October 1962 missile crisis, in which Cuba was 'quarantined' by the US Navy, must have demonstrated both its ultimate vulnerability to the United States and its ultimate dispensability to the Soviet Union. Under the Khrushchev-Kennedy agreement, the Soviet Union undertook to remove Soviet missiles from Cuba, to refrain from sending strategic weapons (including aircraft) there and to reduce Soviet forces to a token number. In return the United States undertook not to invade the island, to respect Cuba's territorial integrity and to control Cuban exiles. But where Cuba's leanings towards communism had troubled its partners in the OAS, its playing host to Soviet missiles alarmed them and produced a much more unanimous condemnation and (for a time) isolation.

Cuba was expelled from the OAS in 1962 and subjected to trade sanctions which forced it more firmly and somewhat reluctantly into the Soviet camp. An attempt by Castro to foster guerrillas throughout Latin America during 1964–9 ended in failure, gaining the full support neither of local communist parties nor of the Soviet government. The soil ought to have been fertile, but except for a few patches it was not.

The third post-war American intervention in Latin America was the despatch of US marines into the Dominican Republic in late April 1965, ostensibly to evacuate American nationals but in fact to restore order after the collapse first of the left-wing reformist government of Juan Bosch and then of the military regime that overthrew it. The OAS agreed to an inter-American force (including US marines) which was withdrawn after the elections of June 1966.

In 1970, the Popular Unity (UP) party led by Allende came to power in Chile. Its overthrow three years later by a military coup is often attributed to the American CIA. There is no doubt that the CIA had an interest in this action, but the UP fell mainly for domestic reasons.[26] It was badly split between left and moderate factions. It failed to satisfy the more extreme left-wing revolutionary groups in the country. It expropriated private enterprise indiscriminately annd inefficiently, offending Chile's own middle class as well as foreign companies and governments, and it took the country to the brink of economic disaster. It antagonised and divided the army. The Allende experience was a lesson to communist and socialist parties in Latin America and elsewhere. It was not the lesson which the Soviet government had earlier forecast: that here was the route to power for all Latin American communist parties. Rather it was a lesson on the power of the right to safeguard its interests and its willingness to use violence to do so.

Throughout Latin America, expanding populations, urbanisation, industrialisation and persistent inter-ethnic divisions have led to stagnating economies and immense social pressures. This has produced smouldering resentments and a multitude of attempts to find solutions to social problems. Many but not all of these have been of the left, and in none except Cuba has the left, as a communist government sympathetic to Moscow, managed to retain power, although recent events in Central America leave the possibility open. Where Cuba was initially the example of the successful rebel, the state that had thumbed its nose at the United States and at American financial power, its success has soured in recent times. The Cuban economy is subsidised by the Soviet taxpayer to the extent of about \$3 billion per year [27] — a process the Soviets are unlikely to repeat elsewhere in Latin America — and when allowed to do so, Cubans emigrate in their scores of thousands. Despite all the aid given it, Cuba is barely a viable Marxist-Leninist society in any sense. It has yet to demonstrate that it has the institutions to survive its leader.

Cuba is nevertheless the success story of Soviet foreign policy in Central and South America, a springboard for political and possibly for military action, a communist society at the front entrance to the capitalist heartland, a continuing thorn in the American flesh. Moreover, while carrying a separate flag, it has become an invaluable ally of and agent for Soviet policies in Africa, playing the paladin champion of proletarian internationalism.

This role has come to be the main factor complicating Cuban and US fitful attempts to improve relations with each other, but it is Cuba's place in Soviet anti-American military strategy that gives the US most cause for concern. The American naval base at Guantanamo on the south-west corner of the island remains, its effectiveness a hostage to Cuban labour and ultimately to Cuban politics. But might Cuba itself come to be the Soviet Trojan horse in the whole region of the Americas, a dagger (to vary the metaphor) pointed at the heart of the West?

After the 1962 Cuban missile crisis, most of the 20 000 Soviet military personnel then in Cuban were withdrawn. In mid-1979 American intelligence began to confirm earlier reports that a Soviet 'combat brigade' of 2–3 000 men was in Cuba, armed with about 40 tanks and other modern military equipment. It was organised and it conducted training as a combat unit. Discreet briefings to members of the US Congress by the State Department were promptly leaked to the press by two senators — Stone of Florida with its large constituency of Cuban exiles, and Church of Idaho, who was then chairman of the Senate Foreign Relations Committee and was believed (correctly, as the 1980 election showed) to be in electoral difficulties. This led to public demands for the removal of the Soviet troops, and to threats that the Senate might use compliance or otherwise with such demands as a basis for deciding whether or not to ratify the SALT II Agreement.

President Carter, with low popularity ratings and battling to get SALT II through, did not need this further embarrassment, but repeated negotiations with the Soviet government brought no concessions. The USSR claimed that the brigade was not a combat unit and would never become one; it was a training centre and was no threat to the United States. Carter was left to make his own excuses and responses, essentially in the form of military plans to demonstrate American superiority in the Caribbean and more economic aid there 'to ensure the ability of troubled peoples to resist social turmoil and possible communist domination'. For reasons that were not quite clear, he also increased the American naval strength in the Indian Ocean.

The Soviet Union must have reasoned that there was more to lose by a second Cuban humiliation than to gain in terms of SALT. To have removed the brigade would have been a dangerous admission of weakness by the regime. It would seem also that Soviet overall strategy for the region required the presence of the brigade to be maintained. The Soviets may well have calculated that anything that weakens American leadership of the Western powers is worth fostering.

Why should the Soviet Union need to retain a small ground combat unit in Cuba? There are several logical reasons. One is that the unit may be needed to protect a Soviet installation on the island. There is such an installation completed or nearing completion — a major new communications-intercept facility (what William Safire in the *New York Times*[28] called 'Brezhnev's big ear' pressed against the coast of the United States to monitor American defence data). A second reason goes back to the Soviet retreat and humiliation in 1962 when no shots were fired. The Soviet government could well have assessed that the United States might wish, on some future occasion, to invade Cuba, not in the inept way attempted in 1961, but as a professional combat operation. The US would be more cautious about doing so if it were to discover that it would be fighting not only Cuba but the USSR. A third reason why the Soviet Union retains this unit relates to the massive Cuban military presence in Africa which may leave President Castro feeling vulnerable to attacks mounted against him either from inside or outside the country. The Soviet brigade would act as a kind of 'praetorian guard' for Castro. A fourth reason could be that the USSR feels it needs a combat unit in a friendly Latin American country in order to mount or support small operations elsewhere in the region. All four reasons are logical and probable.

Cuba is located in an area vital to American security. It is close to the US mainland, to the major naval bases at Key West, Roosevelt Roads (Puerto Rico) and, of course, Guantanamo, and to the large military base at Beaumont, Texas. It lies between these and the Panama Canal through which ships, troops and supplies would normally flow in time of war or high international tension. Control of the Canal has legally been transferred to Panama as from the year 2000.* And although in the event of war Cuba's own bases could be quickly immobilised, in situations short of a US-Soviet conflict the Soviet-supplied Cuban navy and air force as well as the Soviet communications station would be constraining and disturbing factors. In Nicaragua, the Marxist Sandanista government has strong links with both Cuba and the Soviet Union.

While no other state in Latin America at present looks set to become another Cuba, any of the several with left-leaning governments must be considered by the United States to be a potential Cuba, a candidate host for Soviet arms, influence, policies. The Monroe Doctrine is not dead, but it is under heavy constraints. American relations with its southern neighbour, Mexico, are troubled by the number of north-bound emigrants and by a rising Mexican nationalism determined to get the most favourable terms for Mexico's vast newly-discovered oil deposits. The United States is still the most important external power active in Latin America, but the area has changed from being one in which United States policies predominated to one from which the United States could itself suffer disadvantage or even physical attack.

---

* Under the 1977 US-Panama treaty, the United States has the right to 'protect and defend' the Canal.

Although wars derive from perceptions of comparative power, the
absence of war is not necessarily due to a 'balance' of power, nor
the presence of war to an imbalance. Such are the penalties and
uncertainties of war, whether 'won' or 'lost' that a government must
have a strong incentive to resort to force. It must feel that there is
no alternative or that there is much to be gained, or much to lose
from abstention. Most of the time, most countries are at peace and
they prefer it that way whether or not they are stronger than their
neighbours. Even so most wars are, or begin as, wars between
neighbours, and while there has been an absence of war between
the two superpowers these past 35 years, there has not been an
absence of political tension and there have been scores of other conflicts, some of major dimensions, and in a high proportion of them
one or the other superpower has been engaged. At peace though
they are, the two superpowers remain poised and able to destroy
each other, and each other's friends, at a few minutes' notice. There
are in existence nuclear weapons with a destructive capacity equal
to about a million bombs of the kind that destroyed Hiroshima.
With such a horror has the world been living now for many years.

The world has also been living with other horrors, less dramatic
and immediate in their potential but perhaps with greater and more
certain long-term implications. The first is the fact that some hundreds of millions of people live at the level of starvation, and many
more at scarcely above that level. Another is that a profligate use of
natural resources, especially of energy, in the industrialised countries can only add to the global pressures upon such resources for
succeeding generations. A third is the massive deprivation of civil
and political rights around the world.

Each of these bears on questions of military security, although
not in simple or direct terms. Historically, it has not been the really
poor who fight for power or for food, but those on the upward
curve, those who have come to expect more. According to the
Brandt *North-South* report,[1] total global military expenditures are
approaching $450 billion annually, of which over half is spent by the

Soviet Union and the United States, while annual spending on official development aid is only $20 billion. A fraction of the arms expenditures would give the Third World a completely different economic outlook, but unfortunately in the minds of the spending governments the two are not alternatives. It is calculated that one thousandth of the world's expenditure on arms would eradicate malaria. Further, the financing of arms is not a single expenditure figure. There is also the 'opportunity cost' whereby millions of scientists and technicians are employed whose skills could otherwise be used in the alleviation of fundamental living problems.

Contrary to what the Brandt report declares, there is no direct correlation between expenditure on arms, collectively or by individual countries, and the likelihood of war. There is a correlation between arms expenditure and the damage a war would cause if it occurred, but arms can make a nation feel secure, and a roughly equivalent arms build-up by neighbours may actually produce mutual respect and reluctance to engage in conflict. This is not to make a case for heavy expenditure on defence, but it is to acknowledge that in some circumstances to spend too little on proper defence may end up more devastatingly for the populace than to spend too much.

The pressure of population on resources means that nations, as well as commercial non-state actors such as multi-national corporations, will compete for the resources there are, perhaps invoking force to acquire them or to protect what is held. It is not true that there is a fixed quantity of all natural resources heading inexorably to exhaustion. Some are almost inexhaustible, such as solar, wind, tidal or hydroelectric power, or the power from the breeder reactor; some can be recycled; and new technologies may be able to make use of other hitherto unexploited sources. Nevertheless, if population continues to grow at present rates, the world will have nearly 7 billion mouths to feed by the year 2000, and as many again between 30 and 40 years later, and so on. There are limits to the amount of arable ground and to space available for dwellings. History is full of wars over resources or access to them.

It is less easy to relate the enjoyment of human rights to the prospects for peace. Most people in the world, other than in a handful of democracies, are accustomed to the deprivation in varying degrees of civil and political rights. This may bring some grumbling, some dissidence or emigration, but rarely does it produce anything approaching a civil war (which is more often an inter-group contest for civil power rather than a spontaneous demand for 'rights') or intervention by a foreign power. One effect of the presence of democratic rights in the West and their substantial absence in the Eastern bloc is that the Eastern bloc has far greater access to Western military information, to the debates that determine policy (and thus to knowledge about the likelihood and directions of change) than the West has to those of the East. The Eastern bloc countries do not need to debate with their people a change of policy or a national commitment. Such decisions are taken — and are expected by the people to be taken — by the elite, with post hoc unchallenge-able propaganda to support them. This presumably means that the West is more likely to miscalculate the intentions and capacities of the East than vice versa. It means also that pluralistic public debates in the West are usually more of a restraint on controversial political or military action, or on the bald pursuit of national interests, although the voice of the people, not self-evidently the voice of God, may sometimes impel democratic goverments into ill-judged actions.

Constraints on predominance

The strategic balance between the two major power groups co-exists with and is affected by the economic, political and strategic prob-lems of the Third World, or the 'South'. Indeed the major mistake of American governments during the 1970s was to assume that the detente negotiated early in the decade represented not simply a relaxation of direct superpower confrontations but a less assertive Soviet policy everywhere, including towards Third World states, whereas in part the reverse has been true: detente provided the USSR with a relatively secure and untroubled base from which pow-er elsewhere could be exerted. The United States saw detente as the relatively stable situation which would allow extrication from trou-bled and unprofitable commitments in other places. Further, where the US saw detente as a preservation of the central balance, indeed of the status quo, the Soviet Union saw it as an opportunity to re-verse its inferiority within that balance. Strategic predominance, which the United States saw for so long as its proper reward for virtue and the guarantee of the peace in the 'free world', has been greatly attenuated, being shared with maturing allies, with a plural-ity of poor but vocal states, and — even worse — with the unworthy opposition.

Despite the changes in Europe, China, and Japan, the strategic balance remains essentially bi-polar. Japan is at best a middle-ranking, regional military power. China is weighty only in a con-tinental context. European states of the Economic Community and NATO are important partners with each other and with the United States; they pay their fees and maintain their principal. But the United States with its strategic nuclear weapons and immense conventional potential remains the anchor, leader, and essential strength of the West, just as the Soviet Union, less encumbered, is the strength and leader of the Eastern bloc.

To the extent that the East-West strategic confrontation is now or is going to be a confrontation over access to resources, the major competition for the rest of this century will presumably be for oil. Competition will not have to wait for the Soviet Union to become a net importer of oil instead — as at present — of being a substantial exporter. Those exports provide the Soviet exchequer with its main source of hard currency, and it is the continuing or even increasing need of hard currency that may well determine Soviet moves to acquire assured access to foreign oil. That currency is required mainly to import technology and capital for development (including further oil exploration and recovery), as well as food, in which Czarist Russia was much more self-sufficient than the Soviet Union has been.

Had this situation occurred in an earlier century, or early in this one, a Russian government would probably have used its military power to acquire the territory (as in Iran or Iraq) in which major oil fields exist; but today's world is far more complex. There would be no way of telling where such an operation might end, and even if it did not produce a major war, it would certainly destroy the East-West links currently so valuable to the Soviet economy.

The non-communist industrialised powers are providing some of the funds, food and technology which enable the communist states to spend a higher proportion of GNP on arms against which the non-communist states then feel they have to defend themselves. The Soviet invasion and occupation of Afghanistan was much less a challenge to the West than an invasion of Iran would be. It was still a test of the extent to which the Soviet Union could use force outside the European theatre without affecting the flow of Western indirect economic support of Soviet military power. Such was the lack of cohesion of the Western alliance, the interdependence between the lending West and the borrowing East, and the West European concern with its Eastern connections, that the main challenges to the Soviet action came not so much from the West as a group as from the United States which was desperately and only partly successful in mustering its allies, and — less equivocally but less effectually — from the Islamic group of states.

The American response was not particularly out of concern for the people of Afghanistan, but rather due to the fact that the Soviet Union embarked on so flagrant an act of aggression. Almost equally, perhaps, the US was concerned about the continued flow of oil from the Persian Gulf states, which could conceivably be threatened by a stronger Soviet military presence on the eastern borders of Iran. A further incongruity in the Western position became evident:

that although Western European countries (except Britain and Norway) depend on the Middle East for about two-thirds of their oil supplies, they were reluctant to see the United States make military moves in the region of the Gulf in an attempt to prevent anyone from cutting off the oil in case those moves should be seen as provocative by Gulf states which might react adversely to the West, or by the USSR which might make trouble in Europe. Again, despite some limited diplomatic moves in sympathy with the US over its hostages in Iran, the West European states feared that to take such moves too far or to encourage American reprisals against Iran might provoke the Iranian government to invite the protection of Soviet power.

The Western industrialised states have had and still have much to lose from failing to co-ordinate strategy against the oil exporting countries: the spiralling of oil prices, the uncertainty of deliveries, the prospect of political pressure in a crisis. Yet they have been quite incompetent at formulating such a strategy, either through private diplomacy or through agencies such as the OECD or the International Energy Agency (IEA). The oil exporters have also developed greater control over the final destination of oil and are taking over much of the refining, petrochemical and transport operations formerly done by Western companies. OPEC states are using less of their accumulated surpluses in the West to buy costly military equipment, and Walter Levy[2] estimates that by 1985 such surpluses could amount to \$350 to \$450 billion, implying an equivalent deficit in the balance of payments of Western importing countries, with all the problems of recycling. The LDCs, badly hit by oil price rises, have still less capacity to manage the recycling process. The financial and balance of payments problems of Western oil importers may thus outweigh their preoccupations with the East-West strategic balance except in its central confrontation.

The Soviet Union is relevant to these problems, so far, in comparatively minor ways. It is beginning to buy Middle East oil. It has a position of influence in South Yemen (Aden). It occupies Afghanistan and is building up air fields in the south-west. It has treaties with Iraq and Syria. These together give it a position of strength, although certainly not of overwhelming strength, in an area it does not, at this stage, particularly need; whereas the United States, as guardian of Western interests from half a world away, has limited and uncertain footholds in the same areas, the output of which is vital to the West.

Although doubtless the USSR is glad to profit from troubles in and between the Middle East Muslim states, and perhaps to make them a little worse, the fall of the Shah and the potential instability of other oil-producing states have been largely due to forces over which the Soviets have little or no control. These forces include the resurgence of the demand for political power by Islamic religious authorities, aimed mostly at the West, at Western values, and at the modernisation of the state under Western influence. Other complex forces have been let loose, backed by OPEC oil revenues, by anti-colonial political and economic resentments, by Western education, by religious fervour, and by the simple human thirst for power. These forces are by no means all tending in one direction; if externally they are largely directed against the West, they are not therefore more sympathetic to the communist bloc, and domestically they are creating ferments whose outcomes can only be guessed at. In this confusion and potential maelstrom the Western powers are groping uncertainly. The Soviet Union, with no real present need of OPEC oil, is far less engaged but no less watchful, especially of opportunities. It took an opportunity in the Yemen, which gave a clear strategic advantage. It took another in Afghanistan, which has yet to prove whether it is a net gain or loss to Soviet power and influence. The Iraq-Iran war, made possible by superpower arms, has not yet benefited either superpower.

The power of OPEC since October 1973 has forced the United States to review its commitment to Israel. Here again the Soviet Union is barely engaged, except for supplying arms to Syria and Iraq and presumably to the Palestine Liberation Organisation, and stirring up trouble where it can. By encouraging the rapproachement between Egypt and Israel, President Carter helped reduce the prospect of war in the short term, and of Soviet influence in such a conflict. President Sadat's diplomacy, although perhaps unnecessarily critical of his former Arab friends, is producing for Egypt what war could not — the return of the occupied lands including its oil wells. But in the longer term Israel has to live with its other Arab neighbours whose oil revenues (especially Saudi Arabia's and Iraq's) can buy weapons that could destroy most of the Israeli centres of population. By failing to press for a solution to the problem of the Palestinians, and by acquiescing in the Israeli West Bank settlements, the United States has made less likely a long-term peaceful solution, and less likely as well a more stable Arab-Western relationship upon which the vital oil flows depend.

Problems in both alliances

Here, as in other matters, America's European partners have been increasingly disturbed by what they see as the incompetence of American leadership of the West. Mr Carter came in for rather more criticism than his predecessors — his impulsive diplomacy on

SALT II, his vacillation over the neutron bomb, the MX missile, Korea; his failure to grasp the nettle on energy, or to manage the dollar; his attempts to dictate the West's civil nuclear policies — but he was more a symbol than a cause of the malaise in the alliance. There has been an absolute as well as a relative decline in American power, for which Mr Carter can hardly be blamed. For 20 years France has resisted what it saw as the uncertain leadership of an unsophisticated government making unfulfillable commitments. The Federal Republic of Germany under Brandt and Schmidt has become the strongest power in Western Europe, economically and psychologically. It does not want to become a nuclear weapons power, but it wants to be treated by the United States with greater equality; it wants to share the political leadership of the West and, like France, to be able to take initiatives to reduce the appalling power concentrated on the other side of the 'seam of Europe'.

The trouble is that the West Europeans are reluctant to devote the money and effort necessary to provide either a credible conventional or nuclear defence against the Soviet Union. All feel too small under present conditions of technology, and within what is politically possible, to defend themselves singly. So long as the Soviet Union maintains its strength and posture, Western Europe will need America and it will have to continue to pay a price which includes the periodic swallowing of pride and conceding American predominance in the Western alliance.

There are several dangers for the alliance: 1 that France and Germany, especially, will be so concerned with criticising American policy and exerting European initiatives that they will cause the United States to turn away from its wholehearted endorsement of NATO; 2 that they will produce a similar effect in the US by being bemused with their own deals with the Soviet Union and Eastern Europe; or 3 that the US will over-react to Soviet activities; or 4 that the American people will lose confidence in the integrity of their own political leadership, in the capacity of government to cope, in the ability of 'splintered America' to come together in a common cause or to defeat evil and self-seeking vested interests. If any of these were to occur, the already attenuated European confidence in the United States would virtually disappear. One thing is certain: that one day the American troops will go home from Europe. But what European government would wish that to happen while Soviet forces are poised to strike into the West? As it is, the United States has led the West successfully, if somewhat jerkily, for 35 years. There has not been a nuclear war. Despite the traumas of Vietnam and the divisions and 'ingratitude' of Europe, the US has not receded into isolation. Despite — or perhaps partly because of — the power massed on its eastern borders, Western Europe has risen from the ashes of its holocaust to a greater degree of democracy, of economic security, of peace within itself, than it has ever before enjoyed.

The Soviet bloc is not without its problems and they are the unhealthy problems of a closed society, or a series of closed societies each with long histories outside their present association. The dependence on military force rather than on a voluntary consensus for the exercise of leadership must always leave the Soviet government uncertain of its sovereignty. Each time it used or unleashed such force — against East Germany in 1953, Hungary and Poland in 1956, Czechoslovakia in 1968, Afghanistan in 1979 — it alienated supporters world wide and accentuated the iron fist within the communist world. East European partners in the Warsaw Pact can scarcely be unmindful that the Pact forces have been used operationally only against members of the Pact.

The Soviet international exercise of power has been a mixture of successes, uncertainties, and failures: successes in Cuba, South Yemen, Angola, Ethiopia, Vietnam, perhaps Afghanistan; uncertainties in Syria, Iraq, North Yemen, Mozambique; failures in Yugoslavia, Indonesia, Somalia, Egypt, the Sudan, Zimbabwe; and some present successes or uncertainties seem certain to end up as failures. Soviet capacity for military and naval outreach has increased considerably in the past 20 years, as has the ability to use proxies (Cuban armed forces and East German technicians) as agents of Soviet influence. Again the time must come when there will be no Cuban soldiers in Africa, and no Soviet soldiers in Eastern Europe. This is not simply wishful thinking but an assessment of the trends of history. Nationalism is not a new deity but it is increasingly worshipped, and there are 100 or so new states to bow before its shrines. Soviet-style communism initially claimed to divide the world not into nations but into classes. In fact it has deified Russian nationalism while attempting to breach the nationalisms of Eastern Europe, China, Angola and Afghanistan, not by creating a sense of commonwealth but by decreeing a sense of subordination.

This strategy has failed in important ways. It failed first with Yugoslavia. It failed to keep China as a partner; it failed with Albania. It failed to convince the communist parties of Western Europe that Soviet foreign policy was humane and 'correct'. It failed to convince the communist government of Romania that it should keep to the Moscow line. (Romania has now followed Yugoslavia into a closer relationship with the European Community.) It failed to convince the governments of Poland and Hungary that it had the answers to economic progress. It has demonstrably failed throughout all but three or four Third World countries to offer the aid they need or the example they wish to emulate. What the Soviet Union has not failed

to do is to provide a vast war machine capable of ever more universal deployment. Fortunately even so large a machine as this requires
the provision of local facilities and local political sympathy, and the
USSR has found itself no better at stimulating or compelling these
than has anyone else. The time of white man's rule over technologically, educationally and organisationally backward peoples has
largely passed. The logistical and societal dimensions of strategy
are increasingly coming into their own.[3] They give the Third World
states, some of which are skilled political operators, — the power to
resist, if not the power to conquer, a major opponent.

Where the Soviet Union's military and maritime outreach could
be of great benefit to her is in exploiting at present unclaimed or
even unknown resources on the seabed. The United Nations Conference on the Law of the Sea, which has been meeting for seven
years, is edging towards compromise agreements.[4] The area of fundamental difference is in the fact that the industrialised countries
(including the Soviet Union) have the greatest capacity to discover
and exploit the resources, but Third World states believe that they
have a superior claim, because of their poverty, to the wealth so
provided. Both industrialised and developing states accept the proposal that there should be an International Seabed Authority (ISA),
but they have hitherto disagreed: a. as to its role with respect to
production, marketing, and commodity agreements; b. over the activities of the ISA's industrial arm, the Enterprise; and c. over the
extent to which national or private institutions should be given
access. This has become an immensely complex question, and one in
which — however much we may regret it — *force majeure* may come
to play a decisive part.

This could apply equally, though much less immediately, to
Antarctica, the one remaining unexploited continent whose resources are largely unknown and where there are immense problems of extraction through thousands of metres of ice. The present
regime under the 1959 Antarctic Treaty prohibits military activities
in Antarctica and freezes territorial claims (and thus rights to mineral
resources). The Treaty is for 30 years in the first instance. Over a
period of years the Soviet Union has built up a greater number of
research stations and probably a greater quantity of research than
all other nations put together.

Nuclear proliferation

The 'balance of terror' exists because of the nuclear destructive
capacities of the Soviet Union and the United States, capacities so
great that since Nagasaki neither government has been prepared to

use them in even the smallest way for fear of unleashing the whole Armageddon. At least four other states have nuclear weapons or the capacity to produce them: Britain, France, China and India. Whether the British and French weapons consitute a deterrent to Soviet conventional or nuclear attack in Europe is something we do not know, although it is declared British policy to use battlefield nuclear weapons if the British Army of the Rhine is overrun by Warsaw Pact forces. Britain would also use tactical and strategic weapons in a deteriorating situation. China's nuclear weapons are now believed to include ICBMs capable of reaching Moscow and the United States. They diversify the 'threat' to the Soviet Union and must be considered a deterrence to Soviet attack on China. So far as the East-West nuclear balance is concerned, under present circumstances, all three nations' capacities must add weight to the West.

But what of India, and other suspected or potential nuclear weapons states? They are in a different category from Britain, France and China, where nuclear weapons are part of the order of battle. So far as the public record has indicated, India has exploded only one nuclear 'device', i.e. a nuclear bomb. This gives it the capacity, if it so decides, to produce more, and to put them into aircraft from which they could be dropped on neighbouring states. It is hard to see a rationale for such actions, or how an Indian nuclear weapons capacity affects the East-West balance. Without an immense expenditure, India could not compete with China as a nuclear weapons power. No member of either bloc is going to drop a nuclear bomb on India, nor will India drop one on any member of either bloc. The danger from the Indian explosion is the impulse to emulation it has given Pakistan, and thus the prospects of competitive escalation in the sub-continent — an escalation directed against each other. It has been suggested, not very credibly, that a Pakistani bomb, perhaps financed by Middle Eastern or North African states, might be diverted for use against or to threaten Israel. It has also been suggested that Iraq may develop a bomb for the same purpose. So far, Iraq's nuclear programme is consistent with the development of a legitimate nuclear power industry. Israel, where there are no civil applications of nuclear power, has not discouraged reports that it has a secret nuclear weapons capability — reports which no Middle Eastern state, including Libya, can sensibly discount, and which are almost certainly true. Libya and Iraq may well develop the infrastructure of a nuclear industry to provide a weapons option either in response to the threat they believe Israel could pose or, conceivably, in a fanatical attempt to destroy the Jewish state.

The production of energy from nuclear reactors has become increasingly widespread, for obvious reasons, and many states now have the capacity from that basis to develop nuclear weapons if they so wish. Why have they not done so? Reasons will vary from country to country; a common one is the cost. The main reason for the technologically advanced is the fear such an event would generate in any neighbourhood, and the impulse as in South Asia and between the superpowers to unending competitive escalation from which one can only escape by withdrawing from the race and thus wasting virtually every cent spent hitherto. Joseph Nye has pointed out[5] that different political conditions can make the possession of nuclear weapons highly destabilising; also, a country that has just acquired them may be initially less secure by inviting pre-emptive attack.

The Soviet Union has managed the civil nuclear power programme in the Eastern bloc and it has total control over all nuclear weapons in the bloc. So far as is known, it gives no assistance in nuclear technology to any outside country. In the West, nuclear energy technology and equipment are widely available, mostly under safeguards of the International Atomic Energy Agency (IAEA). The Soviet Union, the United States and Britain were all prime movers in the Nuclear Non-Proliferation Treaty (NPT) which was designed in effect to instal a condominium over the production and holding of nuclear weapons. France and China, and some Third World States such as India, refused to sign the NPT and acknowledge the condominium. The NPT prohibits the provision of nuclear weapons technology or materials to other non-weapons states. Moral suasion, common sense and a lack of fear of nuclear attack have brought most nations (including Iraq) to sign and ratify the Treaty.

The Soviet Union has not encouraged the spread, or proliferation, of nuclear weapons. The United States has actively discouraged proliferation, especially in recent years, through fostering the regulating of supplies of nuclear reactor fuels (the London Nuclear Suppliers Group 1974) and through discouraging the recycling of plutonium in thermal nuclear reactors. The first had some effect; the second had little positive effect, as it was discriminatory against particular national programmes including those engaged (as the US itself was and is) in experimental 'breeder' reactors. Like the constraints imposed by the NPT on technology transfer, so the American anti-plutonium regime appeared to other governments to support the commercial interests of nuclear powers as well as their anti-proliferation policies. The launching of the International Nuclear Fuel Cycle Evaluation (INFCE) in 1977 helped the United States share some of the burdens of anti-proliferation activities.

Three other states are often spoken of as moving towards producing nuclear weapons: South Korea, Taiwan and South Africa. South Africa, Israel, India and Pakistan are the only states with nuclear enrichment and/or reprocessing facilities not under IAEA safeguards, and thus able without detection to make weapons grade material. United States' assurances and pressures, perhaps as well as native caution, have restrained the first two states, although if they lost American support they might be tempted to 'go nuclear'. South Africa is much closer than is South Korea or Taiwan to a nuclear weapons option. How would South Africa use such weapons in any foreseeable situation? Should its security be threatened it will not be by a Soviet invasion fleet or massed armies driving overland from the north, but by guerrilla insurgency in South African rural areas, towns and cities. Existing security precautions have coped very well with such activities so far. To use a nuclear weapon against guerrillas would be like using a sledgehammer against mosquitoes. For Taiwan to develop nuclear weapons would be to invite a pre-emptive strike from the mainland. The Republic of Korea is under heavy restraint from the United States, and is most unlikely to go nuclear while the American security treaty is in force. Brazil and Argentina are two other potential nuclear weapons powers, although nuclear facilities in both states are under IAEA safeguards. If either took the step, the other would follow. Their only target is each other. Unfortunately the costly stupidity of either going nuclear is no guarantee that it will not do so.

In the 35 years since Hiroshima, only five more states have acquired nuclear weapons, and their further spread is not inevitable. On present indications any such spread, if limited in extent, might not have a noticeable effect on the central strategic balance although it could be highly destabilising in the immediate neighbourhood.

Since it first appeared as a competition between great powers after World War II, the East-West strategic balance has fluctuated in the comparative strengths of the two power blocs, in the degree of confrontation and in the likelihood of a breach of 'international peace and security'. It has never erupted into direct war. The first major Soviet trial of Western military will was Stalin's blockade of Berlin in 1948–9. The second was when Kim Il Sung, encouraged by Stalin and Mao, tried to take over the whole Korean peninsula. The third was probably the nearest the world has come to nuclear conflict: the October 1962 Cuban missile crisis. Despite the tensions and the dangers and the closeness of the confrontation, no brink was then reached over which mankind almost tumbled to disaster. Yet we will never know how close the world was, through misunderstanding, miscalculation or indeed through calculation, to the brink — to a series of responses and counter-responses of which the ultimate state would have been nuclear catastrophe. As suggested earlier, the Soviet Union made the necessary concessions to the United States over Cuba because the United States was in a predominantly superior conventional situation in the area of confrontation, and had a superior nuclear strategic capacity. For similar reasons, the United States had no ability, even if it had had the will, to challenge the Soviet occupation of Afghanistan. The two superpowers have their areas of sovereignty and control. Khrushchev's mistake was, from a position of weakness, to challenge the United States on virtually its home ground, where it had the support of the regional powers and the Atlantic allies. To challenge from weakness is not a mistake the Soviet Union will make again. When in 1979 the US complained of Soviet combat troops in Cuba, it was the Americans, not the Soviets, who backed down.

The fact that during the 1970s, in matters of military strength, political initiative and national will between two superpowers, the balance shifted in favour of the Soviet Union, does not necessarily mean that the central balance is less secure, or world peace more precarious. The United States and its allies retain enormous deterrent and defensive capabilities. Any fragility would lie in the changed psychology of the two superpowers — the effect which their perceptions of the new balance have on their readiness to take risks or their determination to stand firm, in situations (for example) where the Soviet Union sees an opportunity to expand its territorial, political or strategic control and misreads the extent to which the area is important to the United States; or where the United States seeks to protect by force what it believes to be a vital interest and misreads from a position of inferiority the capacity and intentions of the Soviet Union. Neither of these can be considered even 50% likely, and it is much more probable that, as in the past, the superpowers will not confront each other directly but at one remove. In any case the nature of the balance and the relative capacities of the superpowers are never static. The east Asian balance, in its present form, is comparatively new and is a potential constraint on Soviet initiatives. Whether or not a 'window' exists in American nuclear capabilities — and this is fundamentally a question of Soviet and American perceptions — it would be an irrational, lunatic act for the Soviet Union to launch a nuclear war to take advantage of what is at best a temporary and specialised advantage. On the other hand, for the United States a reworked strategy of variable-level nuclear response supplements but does not replace as a deterrent the ultimate possibility of mutual assured destruction.

The world today is more disturbed and world peace appears less secure because of the shift in the central balance within a whole forest of international problem situations: the Soviet occupation of Afghanistan, unrest in Poland, the aftermath of Iran's holding of the American hostages, the Soviet-Cuban operations in Africa and South Yemen and — more covertly — in central America, especially

Nicaragua and El Salvador, Middle East tensions over Israel and the Palestinians, the Iran-Iraq War, the West's chronic oil situation, Vietnam's imperial adventure which led to its hosting a Soviet military presence, the increasingly mobilised pressures of 'South' against 'North', the pressures of population on resources, the huge numbers of undernourished people, the widespread nature of sub-national terrorism, the appalling plight of refugees, the sharpened assertions of nationalism, of radical Islam as a political ideology, the continued sectarian strife in Northern Ireland, the dozen or more continuing civil wars, the failure of democracy to win support among new nations, the lack of confidence in and between political leaders, the problems of leadership succession, the lack of agreement on arms control, and so on, as well as the instant transmission of news of these matters around the globe. None of these on its own would seem to be a cause of major war. Together they are not necessarily a cause of war but they create a climate of fear, of apprehension, almost an expectation of catastrophe.

One cannot wish away such considerations but it is an abdication of reason to assume the inevitability of disaster. One can take steps to prevent the self-fulfilment of prophesies. For the West, this could involve — so far as it is practicable — matching Soviet nuclear power, but not exceeding it, concurrent with new attempts at arms control, and coming much closer to matching Warsaw Pact conventional power in Europe. It should involve making NATO a different kind of alliance, one not simply for getting the highest common level of agreement under American leadership, but for co-ordinating political and military strategy towards all areas of potential danger including the Middle East. Japan should be brought into such co-ordination. Steps should involve encouraging, broadening and deepening the links of all kinds between Eastern and Western Europe. They should involve renewed efforts at co-operation in managing the world's production and consumption of energy. They should involve new attempts to bridge where possible the 'North-South' gap, and developing strategies to meet more adequately the needs of the South. For the countries of the South, the enormous costs of the East-West strategic balance appear a vast waste of vital resources, and the balance itself offers a political opportunity to play one side against the other. On those elsewhere who see the balance as a prerequisite for peace the obligation lies of working to reduce both the level of armaments and the danger of their being used.

So long as the Soviet Union gives evidence of expanding its military capacity and outreach, and a readiness to use force to extend its power and influence, there will be no substitute for the Western alliance. There will equally be no substitute in Asia for the US-

Japan agreement, which provides a base for America's countervailing power in the Western Pacific, offers physical security for Japan's peaceful development as a democracy, and reassures other states throughout the region that they have no reason to fear a second Japanese imperial venture. The association of China, even informally and psychologically, with this alliance is a major additional factor for maintaining the peace of Asia and for containing Soviet ambitions there and elsewhere.

Peace divisible and fragile

The notion that peace is indivisible is a metaphysical concept at odds with the obstinate world of mortals where peace is eminently divisible. Most states are at peace most of the time yet in any one of the past 30 years there have been several states engaged in international conflict; there have been others where tensions have been building up with the prospect of war; others again where civil wars have been latent or active and engaging the interest of outside powers. The world has also found that it has to live with nationalist or sub-national terrorist organisations operating across borders, perhaps encouraged and supplied by mischievous governments. The central East-West strategic confrontation is not the most volatile but it is potentially the most dangerous and damaging part of this congeries of confrontations, affecting some of them and affected by others.

It is impossible to forecast the prospects for peace or war. Because of the enormous casualties it would inflict, an East-West nuclear exchange would seem to be the least likely of all possible wars. Despite the present Soviet nuclear and conventional force superiority in Europe, conventional war across the dividing line would seem almost equally as unlikely as nuclear war because of the risk that it might quickly turn into a nuclear war. There would seem to be little prospect of a major war in east Asia so long as the present correlation of forces exists. Elsewhere, and above all in the Gulf-Middle East region, there are many places where local conflict exacerbated by superpower vested interests or the taking of opportunities could lead to a wider conflagration. History provides us with all too many precedents, but with no precedent for the ultimate devastation that nuclear weapons could inflict upon a civilisation.

The present uneasy East-West strategic balance has its fragilities or uncertainties as well as its strengths. One uncertainty lies in the forthcoming changes of leadership in several key countries, notably the Soviet Union, China, and North Korea. It is idle to speculate who will succeed the present leaders, how much support they will have, and in what ways their policies will be different. Successions rarely go according to plan. Another uncertainty relates to the implications of new weapons and perceptions about them — the Soviet naval vessels, for example, (see Chapter 1) or chemical or space-directed energy weapons (Appendix A).

There are three areas of what might be called 'system fragility', which if they are badly managed would seriously endanger the strategic balance. One is China with a quarter of the world's population — almost ungovernable, one would have thought. Here is a society emerging from a tyranny whose dimensions are only beginning to be known as long-time political prisoners in their hundreds of thousands return to their families, and staged trials are used to defile the deities. The present leadership has yet to prove that it is more competent or more acceptable than its predecessor. It has to demonstrate that the new pragmatism can mix with the established ideology itself superimposed upon a civilisation developed over several millennia. The reinstatement of Confucius is a symbol both of continuity and of confusion. Which will prevail? There are large numbers of people displaced from their recent authority and they cannot like their reduced status. One may hope that the present order will be maintained but one cannot be at all sure that it will.

Another fragile system — if it is not too diffuse to be called one system — lies between Aleppo and the Straits of Hormuz. This has already been discussed briefly (see Chapter 5). At the heart of it is Saudi Arabia with its tiny population, relatively large number of immigrants, immense oil riches, and its feudal oligarchic government. If that government is replaced by an unsympathetic radical-left regime the consequences could be disastrous for the West. The confusion of confrontations in this whole area — Arabs versus Israel, Egypt versus other Arab states, Arabs versus Jews and Christians in the Lebanon, Sunni versus Alawite in Syria, Iraq versus Iran, Syria versus Jordan, Shiah versus Sunni, fundamental Muslims versus modernist Muslims, and so on — these confrontations leave little grounds for certainty on the balance of power or the resolution of disputes, and there are many factors that make for instability.

A third fragile system of a diffferent kind is the Soviet empire in Eastern Europe. The Warsaw Pact and CMEA formally bind the European states to Soviet political and economic objectives, but the USSR is compelled from time to time to make concessions to the interests of their partners, in both domestic and external matters.[6] What are the lessons of 1953, 1956 and 1968? There are two kinds: that the Soviets will not permit deviance in ideological practice beyond a narrow margin; alternatively, that there are forces operating within East European societies which are prepared to exercise their sovereignty or press for liberal reforms despite that risk. Poland in 1970 showed that its workers had the capacity to force a change of leadership and gain social concessions, but that their own governments would use violence to prevent undue deviation. Poland in 1980–81 has taken this process a long step further, with government uneasily, ambivalently, but nevertheless positively acknowledging the processes of reform. If Soviet divisions intervene to bring Poland back to its knees, they will delay but not eliminate the forces of resistance and reform which are based on spiritual values imbued through the church and strengthened by an intense nationalism.

Although Poland in some ways is a special case, I believe that the events there mark the beginning of the crumbling of the Soviet European system. The process may take 20 years or it could take much less. The longer it takes, probably, the less bloody it will be. The ending of an empire is customarily marked by the imperial government's determined efforts to retain its domains in the belief that the empire is rightly owned, its subjects properly subject; that its loss is being accomplished by trickery and will irretrievably weaken the metropolitan power against its enemies.

It is to be expected that such attitudes will find expression in the Soviet Union during the rest of this century, and they will have some support among East European leaders who owe their position to Soviet power and Soviet-style communist ideology. Whatever governments in the West may feel able in all wisdom to do to help Eastern Europe gain its independence, they must not give credibility to such claims. They must not support the notion that the USSR would be acting in self-defence or as a reasonable projection of power by sending tanks against Polish, Czech or German patriots. It is against such travesties and the system that supports them, as well as for their own protection, that the Western alliances have stood for over 30 years.

APPENDIX A:
ADVANCED WEAPONS SYSTEMS

One must always allow for the possibility that one or the other of the superpowers, or some other technologically-advanced power, may make a weapons breakthrough of the order of the atomic bomb, achieving a superiority so overwhelming as to change the nature of warfare and of the military balance, even if the political implications may be complex.

No government appears to be near such a breakthrough. Both superpowers and some other states are developing new kinds of weapons. A good deal of research has gone into the production of chemical and biological weapons whose impact is not on weapons systems or facilities but on living things — people, animals, plants, etc. The problems associated with the use of biological weapons and the occupation of territory where they have been released are such that (on present estimates) they are unlikely to be employed. Chemical weapons could be valuable in enabling the user to render inoperable a target he is about to overrun. A variety of chemical weapons have been developed and it is widely considered that where nuclear weapons are used chemical weapons will be also. Because of retaliation, chemical weapons are more likely to be deployed against countries with a much lower chemical warfare capacity. As the Soviet Union has put a great deal of effort into chemical weapons, the West has no alternative but to do the same.[1]

Looking further ahead, scientists are considering the possibility of developing weapons with chemicals that can affect behaviour, perception or motor function.

Apart from nuclear weapons (see Chapter 3) the other main development is in space technology. Both superpowers now rely heavily on military satellites in space for reconnaissance and surveillance, communications, missile-launch detection, meteorology, navigation and naval support and other purposes.[2] Most of the Soviet programme of about 100 satellite launches a year is devoted to military purposes. (The United States has about 30 a year.) A treaty in 1967 banned the deployment of nuclear weapons, or other weapons of mass destruction, in space, but there is nothing except a failure of technology or a lack of intent to prevent the destruction of one another's military satellites. Such destruction would have a considerable effect across the whole range of strategic and tactical warfare, both nuclear and conventional.

The two superpowers have developed their anti-satellite (ASAT) systems in different ways and at different rates and the state of the research is kept as secret as possible. Three systems are known to be under development: 1 the use of a small satellite with a high explosive charge to get into the path of a military satellite and destroy it or destroy its external electronic devices; 2 the high-energy laser — a straight energy beam moving at the speed of light. (This has run into major obstacles connected with penetrating the atmosphere without diffusing the beam.) 3 charged particle-beam weapons which consist of streams of protons or electrons accelerated to a very high velocity in an electro-magnetic field and then released in the direction of the target; these also have problems concerned with the atmosphere, although of a different kind.

The 'kill mechanism' of the laser is heat, so a lot of heat may be required; the charged particle beam cuts a hole, like a bullet through cheese, so high accuracy is needed. The United States has used a laser weapon to shoot down an aircraft drone a few kilometres above the earth. The Soviet Union has developed an ASAT satellite capable of destroying vehicles in a relatively low orbit (5 000 metres). No-one as yet seems to have perfected ways to use laser or particle-beam weapons accurately at a distance, or to locate and destroy satellites orbiting at 20 000 km (navigational) or 36 000 km (communications and early-warning). One must assume that the technology will eventually be acquired. The problems of using laser or particle-beam weapons against an incoming ballistic missile are technically solvable but probably not at an acceptable cost.[3] It must also be remembered that all new measures of waging war invariably lead to the development of counter-measures.

ENDNOTES

Introduction

1 Among others, Stephen Garrett, an American political scientist, has made a strong (if not wholly believable) case for the notion that since 1948 the Soviet Union has merely reacted to Western initiatives. ('Detente and the Military Balance', in, *Bulletin of the Atomic Scientists*, Vol. 33, No. 4, April 1977.)

2 The success of American aid to the war-ravaged countries of Europe under the Marshall Plan probably reinforced the US in its assumption that it had the answers to more challenging problems of development.

3 During the 1960s the Soviet government, through increased aid by Warsaw Pact countries, encouraged Third World states to recognise and thus legitimise the government of the German Democratic Republic.

4 One lesson the Soviets have learned: it is better to get someone else to fight for your cause than for you to fight for their's.

5 This figure was given by President Carter in 1979.

6 Paul Keal has defined a sphere of influence as 'a determinate region within which a single external power exerts a predominant influence, which limits the independence of freedom of action of political entities within it'. *Unspoken Rules and Superpower Dominance*, Macmillan, London, 1981.

7 Poland, Czechoslovakia, East Germany, Hungary, Romania, Bulgaria, Mongolia, Afghanistan, in addition to Byelorussia and the Ukraine which are constituted republics of the Soviet Union. Guantanamo is an American base on territory leased from Cuba at a nominal rental under a 1934 treaty which affirms that there is to be no change in status except by mutual agreement.

8 Despite abundant rhetoric on the subject, no American intervention in this century is comparable with Soviet actions in Mongolia, Eastern Europe or Afghanistan.

9 T.B. Millar, *The Indian and Pacific Oceans: Some Strategic Considerations*, Adelphi Paper No. 57, Institute for Strategic Studies, London, May 1969, pp. 4–5.

10 James Cable, *Gunboat Diplomacy, Political Applications of Limited Naval Force*, Chatto and Windus for the I.I.S.S., London, 1971.

11 Barry M. Blechman and Stephen S. Kaplan, *Force Without War: U.S. Armed Forces as a Political Instrument*, Brookings Institution, Washington, 1978.

1 Soviet-Imperial System

1 H. Seton-Watson, *The New Imperialism*, Bodley Head, London, 1968, p. 7.
2 These extensions to Soviet borders were broadly approved by Britain and the US at Yalta, and were confirmed in the Final Act of the 1975 Helsinki Conference on Security and Co-operation in Europe, although neither Britain nor the US has ever recognised Soviet incorporation of the Baltic states.
3 Churchill proposed as a short-term measure that 'predominance' be shared as follows: Romania–Russia, 90 per cent; the others, 10 per cent; Greece–Great Britain (in accord with the USA) 90 per cent; Russia 10 per cent; Yugoslavia 50–50; Hungary 50–50; Bulgaria–Russia 75 per cent; the others 25 per cent. Stalin ticked the paper on which Churchill had jotted these figures. Churchill recorded that this was 'to express the interest and sentiment with which the British and Soviet Governments approach the problems of these countries . . . . It is not intended to be more than a guide, and of course in no way commits the United States, nor does it attempt to set up a rigid system of spheres of interest'. (*Triumph and Tragedy*, Cassell, London, 1954, pp. 198–203.)
4 Including the massacre of thousands of Polish officers at Katyn near Smolensk.
5 Seton-Watson, *The New Imperialism*, Chapter 5. Some authorities believe this is still an open question.
6 Albania had a series of disagreements with Moscow in the late 1950s, became an ineffective member of the Pact in 1961, and was excluded following the Soviet invasion of Czechoslovakia in 1968.
7 *The Military Balance, 1980–81*, p. 14. I am indebted to Geoffrey Jukes for an analysis of the Warsaw Pact command structure 'pecking order', differences in training and doctrine, as well as the limited independent defence production; also to Dale R. Herspring. 'The Warsaw Pack at 25', in, *Problems of Communism*, Vol. XXIX, No. 5, September–October 1980.
8 This feeling was given added depth and weight by the election of a Polish cardinal as Pope and his visit to Poland in 1979.
9 *The New Imperialism*, Chapter 7.
10 This point is disputed by some commentators. The truth is very hard to establish.
11 As a Soviet Foreign Ministry official said to me in Moscow in August 1979, 'Every rock we have, we hold'.
12 Many Western analysts would add the objective of being the dominant superpower.
13 *Encounter*, Vol. LIII, No. 6, December 1979. See also H. Sonnenfeldt and W.G. Hyland, *Soviet Perspectives on Security*, Adelphi Paper No. 150, I.I.S.S., London, 1979; also the two subsequent Adelphi Papers of composite authorship, *Prospects of Soviet Power in the 1980s*, Parts I and II.
14 'Finlandisation' is the notion that by developing unduly close relations with the USSR, and in the absence of effective defence capabilities,

West European states will ultimately find themselves with the same kinds of restraints on foreign and domestic policies as Finland has.
15 Codified in the Helsinki Final Act as 'confidence building measures'.
16 This is a judgement with which many observers of the Soviet system, whether sympathetic or unsympathetic, will not agree. The USSR would almost certainly go to war in an attempt to prevent it.
17 W.G. Hyland, 'Brezhnev and Beyond', in, *Foreign Affairs*, Vol. 58, No. 1, Fall 1979.

2 Anti-Soviet Alliances

1 Belgium, Canada, Denmark, France, Federal Republic of Germany (from 1955), Greece (from 1952), Italy, Luxemburg, Netherlands, Norway, Portugal, Turkey (from 1952), United Kingdom, United States. Iceland is a member but contributes no forces, only the use of its territory for NATO facilities.
2 Just before I went in to address a meeting of the India, Pakistan and Burma Society in the City of London in 1968, the Secretary of the Society said, 'I think you should realise that these gentlemen represent 750 million pounds sterling of British investment.'
3 The Federal Republic recognises 'two states in one Germany'. It accepts the Democratic Republic as a member of the United Nations, and maintains a diplomatic mission in East Berlin.
4 Quoted by Hans-Peter Schwarz, 'Atlantic Security Policy in an Era without Great Alternatives', in, Karl Kaiser and Hans-Peter Schwarz (eds.), *America and Western Europe, Problems and Prospects*, Lexington Books, Lexington, 1977, p. 233.
5 Iceland and Portugal both remained members of NATO (with certain adjustments) when they had communists within the government. Larger states would provide tougher problems.
6 The notion of 'changing NATO from within' raises the reverse considerations, i.e. offering ideological grounds for remaining a member as opposed to nationalist grounds for leaving.
7 This was assumed at the time, and was subsequently confirmed by Khrushchev in his memoirs.
8 The Treaty allowed the United States to deploy forces in and around Japan. It was replaced in 1960 by a new treaty, under which each government undertook to regard an armed attack upon the other as dangerous to its own peace and safety, and to act to meet the common danger. The 1960 treaty was for ten years in the first instance, but it has continued until the present. The wording of the treaty between the US and the Republic of (South) Korea had included a similar commitment.
9 This Treaty, signed 2 December 1954, included the by now standard form of commitment for such agreements: 'Each Party recognises that an armed attack in the West Pacific area directed against the territories of either of the parties would be dangerous to its own peace and safety and declares that it would act to meet the common danger in accordance with its constitutional processes.' It covered the Pescadores as well as

Taiwan. For an analysis and texts of the main extant military treaties see T.B. Millar, *Contemporary Alliances*, Canberra Studies in World Affairs, No. 2, Australian National University, 1981.

10 *The Memoirs of Anthony Eden: Full Circle*, Cassell, London, 1960, p. 102.

11 The Southeast Asia Collective Defence Treaty, subsequently known as SEATO, by the organisation the US reluctantly agreed to being set up. The Treaty provided for joint action against insurgency, and (in accordance with each country's constitutional principles) against 'aggression by means of armed attack' upon any 'designated state' (Laos, Cambodia, South Vietnam, with their consent) or, in the Treaty area, upon member states (Britain, France, the US, Australia, New Zealand, Thailand, the Philippines and Pakistan). By a protocol, the US confined armed action to a situation of communist attack.

12 Undefendable because physical defence would be exhorbitantly costly, because there were many communist cadres already in the south, because of the long, open coastline, and the 'Ho Chi Minh Trail' of routes through Laos to the south.

13 The British and French governments opposed sending a team to Moscow, but their Olympic committees, unofficial bodies, decided otherwise. Note that some American vested interests, such as wheat farmers, also did not share their government's priorities over Afghanistan.

14 It is impossible with any accuracy to give comparative figures of Soviet and American defence spending. There is no rate of comparison between the value of the two currencies in which one can have confidence. Budgets conceal as much as they reveal what is or is not considered spending on 'defence'. Further, Soviet defence production would seem overall to be less efficient than America's, but workers are paid considerably less. On American estimates, the Soviet Union spends roughly 50 per cent more on defence than does the US, and the USSR's GNP is a little over half of that of the US. The American secretary of defence recently reported that Soviet military effort is about 50 per cent larger than that of the US, 'measured by what it would cost to buy Soviet programmes (including personnel) in the US economy'. (*Annual Report for the Fiscal Year 1981*, p. 3.) The difference between Soviet and American investment in military goods (research and development, procurement, and military construction) is even larger. As the secretary states, 'In the past decade, Soviet investment has been cumulatively about 27 per cent larger than ours. In 1979 alone it was probably greater by 85 per cent.' The US Joint Chiefs of Staff *Military Posture* statement for FY1981 says, (p. 29), 'Over the past several years, they [the Soviets] have spent 75 per cent more than the United States for military investment . . . [they] now possess an accumulated military capital stock some 20–25 per cent greater than that of the United States. That differential is projected to increase to 40–60 per cent in favour of the Soviet Union by the mid-1980s'. These figures need a good deal of explanation before their meaning in defence terms is clear. What is clear is that the USSR for some years has been heavily outspending the United States on strategic weapons.

15 As Theo Sommer has pointed out, on Iran this would be unfair criticism. 'European export of military spare parts was stopped early on; the delivery of spares for railway equipment was refused; guarantees for export credits to Iran were withheld; EC diplomats undertook untold demarches on behalf of the unfortunate hostages . . . . For the rest, the Europeans were prepared to go along with the Americans on quite far-reaching measures, provided they served the purpose of freeing the hostages, did not needlessly unite the Arabs with revolutionary Iran, and had the blessing of the United Nations.' ('Europe and the American Connection', in, *Foreign Affairs*, Vol. 58, No. 3, Spring 1979, p. 632.)

3 Soviet-American Nuclear Confrontation

1 United States Department of Defence *Annual Report* FY 1981.
2 'Fratricide' is where an attacking warhead explodes and also destroys one from the same source coming along behind.
3 Some modernisation of the warhead and guidance system is now occurring.
4 All Minuteman silos and launch-control centres are hardened.
5 NATO code names.
6 Range figures are complex and depend on the load carried, in-flight refuelling, and the flight pattern. On an average one could reasonably calculate the radius of action of an aircraft to be about one-half of its range.
7 Testimony before the US Senate Foreign Relations Committee. It must be remembered that ICBM sites and other military targets are sometimes close to centres of population. A Soviet counter-force first strike would destroy 5–20 million Americans. An American strike against Soviet silos and military targets would have a comparable effect.
8 Although even without their ALCMs, B52s are useful weapons systems, especially if employed after SLBMs and ICBMs had inflicted substantial damage on Soviet defence installations.
9 The agreement allows until 31 December 1981 to complete the reduction to 2 250.
10 *Department of State Bulletin*, Vol. 79, No. 2028, July 1979, p. 60.
11 Some of these instances are cited in the State Department Special Report No. 55, *Compliance with SALT I Agreements*, issued July 1979. A more generous interpretation is that the Soviets were 'stretching' Treaty obligations rather than knowingly violating them.
12 The SS-20, which is the first two stages of the SS-16, is already positioned for use against Western Europe. Some 150 are said to be deployed, and the US is having difficulty in locating them. About 100 are considered to be positioned against NATO.
13 There have been proposals to build a large number of new Minuteman silos in among existing silos and to move the missiles around periodically in order to disguise where they are at any given time. If desired, the MX could later be exchanged for the Minuteman.

14 There are varying views as to how extensive the Soviet civil defence measures are and how effective they would be. They include not only shelter systems, but also programmes for evacuation, dispersal and relocation of city populations, factories, etc. and hardening of industrial facilities. One 1977 Western estimate was that, with six hours' advance notice and assuming optimum conditions (such as weather and responsiveness of population) some 70 per cent of the population could be evacuated within a period of 3–4 days, and 30 per cent of them dispersed. It is most difficult to credit such figures. There have been few civil defence exercises, and these mostly in small cities, and with mostly a poor response. The shelter programme seems designed primarily to protect essential personnel, but it is much more extensive than would be required just to do that. The United States, on the other hand, long ago abandoned a policy of providing shelter for the civil population. Soviet civil defence measures would offer little protection in the event of a sudden US first strike, rather more with a few days warning, and would be most useful in the event of protracted nuclear war. But in any of these situations, many millions of Soviet citizens would be killed.

15 Vertical proliferation is the development of more sophisticated and effective nuclear weapons. Lateral proliferation is the development of nuclear weapons by an increasing number of states.

4 Military Equation in the European Theatre

1 The Pershing 1 has limited refire capacity. It is understood that the SS-20 has several missiles, each with three warheads, provided for every launcher.

2 See 'The East-West Threatre Balance in Europe', in, *The Military Balance 1980–81*, pp. 110–15.

3 *Defence in the 1980s*, Statement on the Defence Estimates 1980, Vol. 1. HMSO, London, Cmnd 7826–1, para. 211. The Chevaline programme includes improved capacity to manoeuvre missiles in space, and to penetrate Soviet anti-ballistic missile defences.

4 From time to time it is proposed (usually by a Frenchman) that France and Britain combine their nuclear forces into a European nuclear force, thus 'decoupling' the European security situation from the Soviet/American strategic nuclear confrontation.

5 Sir John Hackett and others, *The Third World War: August 1985*, Sphere Books, London, 1979.

6 Address to a conference in Brussels convened by the Center for Strategic and International Studies, Georgetown University, (Washington, D.C.), 1 September 1979. Official transcript, p. 10.

7 NATO Nuclear Planning Group Final Communiqué, 14 December 1979. On 17 June 1980, the British government announced that 160 US GLCMs would be based in southern England from 1983.

5 Areas of Potential Danger

1 The following states are members of the Organisation of Petroleum Exporting Countries (date of joining is shown in parentheses): Iraq (1960), Venezuela (1960), Saudi Arabia (1960), Iran (1960), Kuwait (1960), Qatar (1961), Indonesia (1962), Libya (1962), Abu Dhabi[a]/UAE (1967), Algeria (1969), Nigeria (1971), Ecuador (1973), Gabon[b] (1975). Membership of the Organisation of Arab Petroleum Exporting Countries are the above, less Venezuela, Iran, Indonesia, Nigeria, Ecuador and Gabon, plus Egypt.
(a) Membership transferred in 1974 to United Arab Emirates (which Abu Dhabi joined); (b) Became associate member in 1973 and full member in 1975.

2 As reported in *The Christian Science Monitor*, International Edition, 3 December 1979.

3 The extremely complex web of world energy production and consumption is indicated by the fact that when Iran reduced its export of gas to the Soviet Union, this hit Soviet export of gas to Eastern and Western Europe. Czechoslovakia, West Germany, Austria, France, Italy, Belgium and the Netherlands are now substituting Algerian gas from a trans-Mediterranean pipeline.

4 They suggest an economic growth rate of about 3 per cent p.a., but some observers estimate a much lower rate than that.

5 Article V prohibits the formation in their respective territories of groups hostile to the other country. Article VI states, 'If a third party should attempt to carry out a policy of ursurpation by means of armed intervention in Persia or if such Power should desire to use Persian territory as a base of operations against Russia, and if a foreign Power should threaten the frontiers of Federal Russia or those of its allies, and if the Persian government should not be able to put a stop to such menace after having been once called upon to do so by Russia, Russia shall have the right to advance her troops into the Persian interior for the purpose of carrying out the military operations necessary for its defence. Russia undertakes, however, to withdraw her troops from Persian territory as soon as the danger has been removed.' An explanatory note from the Soviet government showed that the Articles referred only to preparations by the supporters of the Tsar for 'a considerable armed attack' upon Russia or for establishing a base of operations in Persia (Iran).

6 Reported in *Truman Speaks*, Columbia University Press, New York, 1960, p. 71. Averill Harriman said later that Britain took the initiative to make the Soviet Union withdraw, but was strongly backed by Truman. The Soviet government had demanded self-rule for Iranian Azerbaijan, Soviet oil rights in five northern provinces of Iran, and Soviet troops to be stationed permanently in parts of the country.

7 This was variously reported, although the substance is much the same. On 3 March 1959, Dr Sadr, Parliamentary Under-Secretary of the Iranian Foreign Ministry, declared Articles 5 and 6 of the 1921 Treaty to be 'null and void.' On 5 November 1979, the revolutionary government of Iran announced that it had abrogated the 1959 US-Iran defence agree-

ment and Articles 5 and 6 of the 1921 Russia-Persia treaty.

8 Official text of address as delivered. A Pentagon spokesman subsequently said that such force would not necessarily exclude nuclear weapons.

9 See, for example, John M. Collins and Clyde R. Mark, 'Petroleum Imports from the Gulf: Use of US Armed Force to Ensure Supplies'. A more recent British professional analysis of the problems of safeguarding the supply of oil from a 'Saudi core' area comes to similar conclusions. See Sir John Hackett, 'Protecting oil supplies: The Military Requirements', a paper given at the 22nd Annual Conference of the International Institute for Strategic Studies, September 1980. Hackett refers to the vital need to pre-position troops for early action, with appropriate facilities, and to provide adequate air and sea mobility for the rapid deployment of a main force.

10 I am indebted to Dr Mohammed Ayoob for a comprehensive analysis of the roots and implications of the conflict. 'Conflict in the Gulf — A Background Report', *Pacific Defence Reporter*, Vol. VII, No. 4, October 1980.

11 General Pavlovsky had directed the Soviet military invasion of Czechoslovakia in 1968.

12 Article 4 calls for Afghanistan and the Soviet Union to 'consult with each other and take by mutual agreement appropriate measures to ensure the security, independence, and territorial integrity' of both states.

13 Quoted in 'Afghanistan', London, Foreign and Commonwealth Office *Background Brief*, January 1980.

14 The first Russian port on the Pacific was Okhotsk, established in 1649. Peter expanded Russian territory in the Pacific region.

15 US Department of State, *Nazi-Soviet Relations 1939–1941*, Washington, 1948, pp. 251–9.

16 Pakistan rejected the initial offer of American arms after the Soviet invasion, but presumably would seek such help if under direct Soviet threat.

17 The latest was in 1976, proposing joint Soviet-Turkish control.

18 Parties to the Convention were the United Kingdom, France, Greece, Japan, Turkey, USSR, Yugoslavia, Romania, Bulgaria, and (surprisingly) Australia.

19 Turkish soldiers taken prisoner in the Korean War withstood harsh conditions and attempts at indoctrination better than any other national group.

20 By 1978 Turkey had become the largest non-communist recipient of Soviet aid. Under the Soviet-Turkish Treaty on Good-Neighbourly Relations, signed in 1972 and reaffirmed in 1978, both states undertook to deny the use of their territory for aggressive or subversive activities directed against the other. The Soviet Union tried, unsuccessfully, to invoke this clause in order to prevent the reopening of American facilities in late 1978.

21 See Andrew Wilson, *The Aegean Dispute*, Adelphi Paper No. 155, 1979, I.I.S.S., London.

22 In fact, despite public statements to the contrary, it appears that many

of these were kept operational, on the grounds that they were NATO rather than American facilities.

23 Greece, with its own version of ostpolitik, now imports sizable quantities of oil from the Soviet Union and from Libya. Some Soviet merchant vessels are repaired in Greek shipyards.

24 On arrival in Belgrade in November 1976, Brezhnev said that the Soviet Union had no intention of attacking Yugoslavia. This was a fairy tale invented in the West, he said, like the story of Red Riding Hood and the Wolf. Although he may have meant well, the Yugoslavs did not find the comparison reassuring.

25 An outsider may also suspect that the alert was intended as a warning to any dissident elements within Yugoslavia, and a call to the Yugoslav people to unite and face up to the difficult situation ahead.

26 As in 1941, Bulgaria would probably leap at the opportunity to acquire at least Macedonia for itself.

27 After repeated Soviet requests, Yugoslavia in the early 1970s gave the Soviet navy the right to service two diesel submarines at a time at the southern port of Tivat. In 1978 the US Navy was given a similar right to one cruiser-class vessel.

28 It was Yugoslavia, and especially Tito, that prevented Cuba as chairman of the 1979 NAM conference from getting the movement to espouse the view that the USSR is its 'natural ally'.

29 Without the use of chemical or nuclear weapons, it would take many divisions (estimates run as high as 60) to subdue a defiant Yugoslavia.

30 Tito threatened to use the army against Croatian nationalists in 1971, and deployed it publicly in Zagreb, the Croatian capital.

31 The official Yugoslav figure is 276 000 plus the whole nation as reservists.

32 When President Tito visited Washington in March 1978, the communiqué of the two Presidents included the following sentence: 'President Carter reiterated the lasting support of the United States to the independence, territorial integrity, and unity of Yugoslavia'. On 18 January 1980, a US State Department spokesman reaffirmed that support and indicated that the form it would take was the subject of long-standing agreement with the Yugoslav government. The point was made again after the death of Tito.

33 In the novel *The Third World War* by Sir John Hackett and others, the war begins in Yugoslavia in July 1985 after a clash between the Slovenian Republic government and the federal government in Belgrade instigated by a Soviet inspired Committee for the Defence of Yugoslavia. The Committee calls for Soviet military assistance, which is promptly given (from Hungary and the air), but brings an American response (marines and airborne forces from Italy).

6 Areas of Strategic Competition

1 In 1979, France removed 'Emperor' Bokassa of the Central African Republic, Tanzania removed President Amin of Uganda, and the army

of Equatorial Guinea deposed its dictator, President Macias.

2 In 1977 a senior South African official talked to me about the 'communist black belt' across Africa, i.e. Angola, Zambia and Mozambique. When I protested that this seemed too simplistic an assessment, he went on, 'And now they've got Tanzania', a deduction from the fact that Soviet President Podgorny was then visiting Dar-es-Salaam.

3 *International Herald Tribune*, 13 June 1980.

4 They had Soviet arms, and apparently Cuban support. See Bayard Rustin and Carl Gershman, 'Africa, Soviet Imperialism and the Retreat of American Power', *Commentary*, Vol. 64, No. 4, October 1977.

5 Some 16 000 Cuban troops and about 1 000 Soviet military advisers were in Ethiopia at this time.

6 South-West Africa, a former German colony, was a 'C' class mandate administered by South Africa after World War I, and was retained under South African administration after World War II despite United Nations resolutions and International Court rulings.

7 Of South Africa's population of 26 million, 16.5 per cent are white, 9.3 per cent 'coloured', 2.0 per cent Asian, and 71.3 per cent black.

8 The point is discussed by Robert S. Jaster, *South Africa's Narrowing Security Options*, Adelphi Paper No. 159, I.I.S.S., London, Spring 1980, pp. 44–48.

9 For the strategic implications of the straits, see T.B. Millar, *The Indian and Pacific Oceans: Some Strategic Considerations*.

10 This information is a personal assessment based on figures from a variety of official and other sources, including United States *Military Posture for FY 1980*. The Soviet divisions, which were substantially increased following the Sino-Soviet clash at Damansky Island in 1969, have varying degrees (or categories) of combat-worthiness, but an unofficial observer cannot know what is the state of particular divisions. The Chinese figures are taken from what appears to be an official report printed in the evening edition of *Mainichi Shimbun* (Tokyo) 13 October 1978. Note that *Asian Security 1980*, published by the Research Institute for Peace and Security in Tokyo, lists 34 Soviet divisions in the Far East, totalling over 350 000 men, the remaining divisions presumably being in the Siberian Military District and facing the Chinese western border. Figures of Soviet naval vessels were taken from this publication.

11 It is doubtful that there would be sufficient warning to use the extensive shelter systems in a number of Chinese cities, or that they would be more than a palliative.

12 See 'State Department Report on Normalisation Negotiations with China', in Congressional Research Service, *China and Asia — An Analysis of Recent Policy towards Neighbouring States*, Washington, 1979, pp. 43–5.

13 Japan managed to get into the Treaty (Article 4) a statement that it would not 'affect the position of either contracting party regarding its relations with third countries'.

14 Some observers doubt whether this incident had the support of the Chinese government.

15 On the economic side: about a third of South Korea's imports come

from Japan, and Japanese firms account for 55 per cent of all foreign investment in the country. *Asiaweek*, 6 June 1980.

16 *ibid.*

17 A popular post-war song for many years in Japan, 'China Nights', proclaimed the affections of a Japanese soldier, serving in China, for his Chinese girlfriend.

18 Even in a crisis such as an invasion, there were doubts about the SDF's legal capacity to open fire.

19 Under the Shimoda Treaty of 1855, the island of Sakhalin was a joint Russian-Japanese possession and in the Kurils the boundary between the two states was drawn between the islands of Etorofu (Iterup) and Uruppu (Urup). By the Treaty of St Petersburg (1875), Japan ceded to Russia the northern half of Sakhalin, in return for the northern islands of the Kuril group. In 1945, Soviet forces occupied the whole of Sakhalin and all the Kurils, including Etorofu and Kunashiri plus two islands adjacent to the Japanese mainland (i.e. Hokkaido) Habomai (more correctly the Habomais — a small group) and Shikotan, which had never been considered part of the Kuril chain. The United States in 1955 declared them to be part of Hokkaido, and in a joint declaration of 19 October 1956 the Soviet Union agreed to turn over the Habomais and Shikotan to Japan when a treaty of peace between the two countries was signed. After the 1960 revision of the US-Japan Security Treaty, the Soviet government declared that to return the Habomais and Shikotan to Japan would only be considered after the removal of all foreign (i.e. US) troops from Japan. (Rodger Swearingen, *The Soviet Union and Post-war Japan: Escalating Challenge and Response*, Hoover Institution Press, Stanford, 1978, pp. 189–90, 193–4. *Japan Times Weekly*, 13 October 1979.

20 This is according to the statistical processes used by the Japanese government which has an interest in showing the electorate that it is restrained in its defence spending. If calculated on the same basis as used in NATO countries, Japan's defence costs would be about 1.6 per cent of GNP.

21 *United States Military Posture for FY 1980*, p. 15. The FY 1981 edition does not repeat this information presumably because of detachments to the (Persian) Gulf. According to Lieutenant-General Loving, Commander of US Forces in Japan, these forces have 123 separate facilities, rent free, employing a Japanese labour force of about 21 000. In FY 1978 Japan supported the US force costs to the extent of $548 m. This has since been substantially increased. Testimony to US Senate Committee on Armed Services, 20 February 1979, p. 730.

22 Report 'On the Guidelines for Japan–United States Defense Cooperation', issued by the Japanese Ministry of Foreign Affairs and Defense Agency, 20 November 1978.

23 In the US Defence Department *Annual Report FY 1981*, p. 50, Defence Secretary Harold Brown referred to Japan as 'the keystone of our security position in the Far East.'

24 Japan denounced the taking of the hostages, and did not send an Olympic team to Moscow; it suspended a number of meetings with the USSR, shelved negotiations on new Siberian development projects, stopped

high technology transfers, increased defence spending, and in general formed a common front with the European Community vis-à-vis Iran. Although for a time it bought increased quantities of Iranian oil, it later ended such imports on the grounds of price.

25 *The Times*, 11 July 1980.

26 Soviet comment on the overthrow of Allende is remarkable for the extent to which, at the time, it did not blame the United States. See Leon Gouré and Morris Rothenberg, *Soviet Penetration of Latin America*, University of Miami Center for Advanced International Studies, Miami, 1975, pp. 102–120.

27 This figure (about $8 m per day) was given by President Carter in late 1979. It includes Soviet payment of five times the world price for Cuban sugar, and supplying Cuba with virtually all its oil imports at about 60 per cent of the OPEC price.

28 *International Herald Tribune*, 7 September 1979.

7 East-West Strategic Balance

1 *North-South: A Programme for Survival*, Report of the Independent Commission on International Development Issues, (Willy Brandt, Chairman), Pan Books, London, 1980, pp. 117–8.

2 See Walter J, Levy, 'Oil and the Decline of the West', in, *Foreign Affairs* Vol. 58, No. 5, Summer 1980.

3 See Michael Howard, 'The Forgotten Dimensions of Strategy', in *Foreign Affairs*, Vol. 57, No. 5, Summer 1979.

4 In December 1970 the UN General Assembly adopted (Resolution 2749 (XXV)) principles for the exploitation of the seabed and its resources beyond national jurisdiction, designating the area and its resources as the 'common heritage of mankind'.

5 Joseph S. Nye, 'Maintaining a Non-Proliferation Regime', in, *International Organisation*, Vol. 34, No. 4, 1980.

6 See Dale R. Herspring, 'The Warsaw Pact at 25'.

Appendix A

1 See Amoretta M. Hoeber and Joseph D. Douglass, Jr., 'The Neglected Threat of Chemical Warfare', *International Security*, Vol. 3, No. 1, Summer 1978.

2 See 'Military Competition in Space', *Strategic Survey 1978* I.I.S.S., London, pp. 23–9.

3 Lieutenant-Colonel Barry L. Thompson states that, if perfected, direct energy (i.e. lasers or particle beams) weapons operating from satellites against offensive ballistic missiles would provide a high degree of protection. They could also have a valuable offensive capability. ('Directed Energy Weapons and the Strategic Balance', in *Orbis*, Vol. 23, No. 3, Fall 1979.) There is no public evidence yet that such weapons are anywhere near to being perfected.

INDEX